Printed at the Mathematical Centre, 413 Kruislaan, Amsterdam.

The Mathematical Centre, founded the 11-th of February 1946, is a non-profit institution aiming at the promotion of pure mathematics and its applications. It is sponsored by the Netherlands Government through the Netherlands Organization for the Advancement of Pure Research (Z.W.O.).

DETERMINISTIC TOP-DOWN AND BOTTOM-UP PARSING:

HISTORICAL NOTES AND BIBLIOGRAPHIES

ANTON NIJHOLT

MATHEMATISCH CENTRUM   AMSTERDAM 1983

ISBN 90 6196 245 5

CONTENTS

PREFACE

The theory of parsing was initiated in the sixties by the pioneering works of Lewis and Stearns, Knuth, Floyd, and Wirth and Weber. In the seventies a vast body of knowledge has been obtained in the three subfields to which the three bibliographies in this monograph are devoted, viz. top-down parsing, LR-grammars and parsing, and precedence parsing.

The total number of entries in these bibliographies exceeds thousand references, dealing primarily with theoretical problems, but also with more application oriented issues such as compiler construction techniques.

Anton Nijholt has performed an admirable job in collecting the material in these bibliographies. Based on his extensive research in parsing theory, he is eminently qualified for this work, and we expect that the further development of the theory of parsing will benefit substantially from his efforts.

Amsterdam, September 1982

Jaco de Bakker.

I think that I shall never see
A string as lovely as a tree.
For strings are made by fools like me,
And only parsers make a tree.

A string just lies there, plain and flat,
As boring as a welcome mat--
A rather dreary, flabby sight,
Of symbols stretched from left to right.

....

Some parsers gaily go to town,
Working from the root on down.
While others go from top to bottom,
Assigning forms to strings that's got em.

....

And there are parsers that are able
To drive constructions from a table,
Keeping guesses good and warm
With hints in Backus-Naur form.

....

(Parts from a poem on Trees by Peter Kugel,
SIGACT News, April 1975, page 19)

1. INTRODUCTION

1.1. General

In this Monograph three bibliographies on parsing are presented. These bibliographies are on *top-down* parsing *LR* parsing and *precedence* parsing, respectively. Although these bibliographies are mainly concerned with the theoretical issues related with parsing for (deterministic) context-free languages, several other aspects, e.g. compiler construction, have found their place in these bibliographies.

Languages are defined by grammars which give the syntactic definition of the language. Following Chomsky, in computer science grammars are generating systems. The task of parsing is to determine whether a given string of symbols is element of the language and, if so, to make the syntactic definition with respect to the grammar explicit. The latter can be done by showing how the given string can be generated by the syntactic rules of the grammar.

After the discovery of the correspondence between the definitions which were introduced by Chomsky[4] and the notation of the programming language ALGOL 60 (BNF, which stands for Backus Naur Form[1]) an enormous number of publications appeared in which properties of languages, grammars and parsing methods are discussed. Floyd[5] showed that, in general, programming languages are not context-free languages. However, considerable parts of programming languages can be described with context-free grammars. Therefore research concentrated on this class of grammars and languages and more general formalisms sometimes were obtained as generalizations which were based on the context-free grammars. The availability of a mathematical formalism led to a situation where theory was being developed which did not necessarily yield results which were applicable in computer science.

The need for a parsing method and a parser becomes clear whenever the use of a language is formalized in order to be able to communicate with hard- or software. For such an application it is not only necessary to investigate whether a given string of symbols is syntactically correct, but also the *meaning* which is associated with the string should be understood by the hard- or software. Therefore, in the case of a programming language, the parser is only part of a more complicated piece of software, the compiler, which translates the sentences (commands, statements, programs) of the user to another language which can be understood by the hard- or software.

In 1956 the first FORTRAN compiler was built. This compiler took about 18 man years to develop. Nowadays the building of a compiler for a programming language will take considerably less time. One of the reasons is that it has become customary to modularize the process of compilation into several phases such as e.g. lexical analysis, syntax analysis (parsing), code generation, error handling and code optimization. Because of this modularization several research areas have become prosperous and tools have been developed which can be used in the construction of each of these modules. Especially the automatic generation of lexical analyzers and parsers from the syntax of a language is no longer considered a big problem. The construction of the other parts of a compiler still asks for further formalization of the available methods. The attempts to automate the production of those parts of a compiler which deal with semantics (code generation) are based on certain enrichments of context-free grammars. Formalisms which are used are, among others, Van Wijngaarden grammars, affix grammars, attribute grammars and denotational semantics. Van Wijngaarden's formalism has been used in the definition of ALGOL 68 [12]. Affix grammars and attribute grammars were introduced by Koster[8] and Knuth[7], respectively. Presently, the use of these types of grammars in compilers and compiler writing systems is receiving considerable attention. See e.g. the bibliography on attribute grammars compiled by Raiha[10]. In the course of the years compilers and compiler writing systems have been used for the translation and the development of programming languages, languages for editors and text processing, languages for file handling, relational data base managers, picture generation etc.

1.2. Parsing Theory

Parsing theory is part of formal language theory. Mathematical linguistics and the design of programming languages such as ALGOL have been the two main sources from which formal language theory has been developed. As stated by Greibach[6], until 1964 formal language theory still could be considered part of mathematical linguistics. After 1964 formal language theory developed as a branch of theoretical computer science.

From the point of view of parsing theory it is possible to distinguish the following three periods:

- Some theory and ideas are available from mathematical linguistics. However, compiler builders start (almost) from scratch and develop *parsers* as part of compilers for specific languages and computers. Ideas which were used were not always written down, partly because parsing was not always distinguished from the other parts of a compiler. First the interest focused on parsing and compilation of arithmetical expressions (formulae). Later it was recognized that this was only part of a more general problem of compiling programming languages (see Bauer[2]).

- Formal language theory is being developed. Models of compilers and theories concerning parsing are developed. Ideas which had been used by compiler builders were formalized into parsing methods. The theory starts to raise its own questions. It becomes possible to distinguish between engineering activities and scientific progress. In this period we can find the birth of the three parsing methods, **LL(k)**, **LR(k)** and **precedence** parsing, which are covered by this Monograph. The first compiler writing systems are built. Top-down (recursive descent) and precedence oriented systems can be recognized. At the end of this period the first LR-based system is constructed.

- The framework is available and is used to embed new and old questions with both practical and theoretical considerations. Techniques are further formalized and generalized. New and sometimes better proofs appear for old results. Developments in formal language theory are reflected in parsing theory. For example, parallel rewriting systems, parsing in parallel environments and especially complexity considerations are topics which acquire attention. While in the second period we see that *methods* for parser construction replace *ideas* which appeared in the construction of ALGOL 60-like programming languages, we now can distinguish, after having seen the construction of some ALGOL 68 compilers, the growth of methods for the parsing of two-level grammars and certain classes of grammars which can be considered as subclasses of the two-level grammars (e.g. the affix and attribute grammars).

Wegner[11] distinguishes three phases of programming language development, corresponding roughly to the 1950's, 1960's and 1970's. These phases are *discovery* and *description* of concepts, *elaboration* and *analysis* of concepts and software *technology,* and are characterized by an *empirical, mathematical* and an *engineering* approach, respectively. These phases can also be recognized in the area of parsing and its applications. During the 1970's many parser generators were constructed and used as a tool in programming language development. For example, LL(1) and LR(1) based parser generators have been developed for use on the wellknown UNIX-system. Moreover, this engineering approach has stimulated research in the parsing of ambiguous grammars and attribute grammars.

1.3. Contents of the Bibliographies

LL(k), LR(k) and simple precedence parsing methods are the most widely used methods for parsers and parser generating systems. Mostly these methods are used in a slightly restricted or a slightly generalized form. LL(k) parsing is a top-down parsing method, the others are bottom-up parsing methods. Both top-down and bottom-up methods have been used in the early years of compiler (writing systems) technology. During a rather long period in the 1970's LR-parsing has received considerable attention, both in theory and in practice. However, the last few years have also shown the development of some LL(1) based systems. Although there are interesting exceptions (e.g. in Japan, USSR and West-Germany) precedence oriented systems seem to have lost the interest of those who develop compilers and compiler writing systems. Nevertheless, like the LL- and LR-methods the precedence method is still one of the fundaments of parsing theory. Therefore these three methods are dealt with in the bibliographies of this Monograph. Parsers in working compilers have been constructed using *production-language*. Except for a few references this implementation method has not been considered in the bibliographies. Obviously, there are many other parsing methods. When such a method resembles deterministic top-down parsing references can be found in the top-down bibliography. Similarly, some other deterministic bottom-up methods can be found in the LR- or precedence bibliographies. It follows that some references can be found in more than one of the bibliographies.

When you're looking for a reference and you don't know which bibliography to consult then first try the LR bibliography, next the top-down bibliography and, finally, the precedence bibliography. The area of general context-free parsing is not considered in this Monograph. However, some references to classical papers (Earley, Kasami, Valiant and Younger) and a more recent paper by Graham, Harrison and Ruzzo can be found in the LR-Bibliography.

There exist many non-context-free parsing methods. Some of these, especially those which have found practical application and which are related to the three methods treated here, are mentioned in the bibliographies. There exist various *non-conventional* parsing techniques. The obvious example is parsing in parallel computational environments. For natural languages (speech) special parsing methods, e.g. the use of *augmented transition networks*, have been developed. Another formalism which should be mentioned and which does not appear in the bibliographies is an extension of the context-free grammars, the so-called *definite clause grammars* (Pereira and Warren[9]). These grammars are a special case of a formalism introduced by Colmerauer. The definite clause grammar of a language can be considered as a program in the programming language PROLOG. When this program is executed it behaves as a top-down parser. Writing parsers in PROLOG has been made simple since it is possible to use a so-called grammar rule notation.

Each rule can be provided with arguments which make it possible to add non-context-free and semantic information in the parser.

Attempts have been made to compare the LL, LR and precedence parsing methods. A grammar for a programming language can be designed for especially one of these methods. In that case the other methods are not necessarily suitable for this grammar. Observations on the parsing method and resulting small manual changes in the grammar can already lead to an enormous reduction of time and space requirements of the parser. On the other hand, when a parsing method is selected for inclusion in a compiler writing system it is necessary to base the choice on general properties of the parsing methods and on the programming language grammars to be expected. Among others, when parsers are to be generated automatically, it is necessary to consider the theoretical generality of the method, the possibility to work for *natural* grammars for programming languages, the space and time requirements of the resulting parsers, the possibility to optimize the parsers, the possibility to include, automatically, error detection, correction and recovery methods in the parser, and the possibility to handle the semantics which is associated with the grammar rules.

Among others, the following topics are covered by the references.

a. equivalence properties of language classes, language hierarchies, intercalation theorems, properties of parse trees, grammatical covers, grammar forms, grammatical inference

b. relationships between grammar classes, transformations between grammar classes, generalizations of LL- and LR-grammars for other than context-free languages, deterministic translation grammars, LL- and LR- attributed grammars, decidability and complexity results for deciding whether a grammar belongs to a certain family of grammars

c. relationships between parsing methods, unifying approaches of parsing methods, sizes of parsers, parser optimization, time and space complexity of parsing methods, parsing methods used in compilers and compiler writing systems, error handling (detection, correction and recovery), the design of parsing grammars for programming languages, incremental parsing, parsing in parallel environments, parsing of two-level grammars

The bibliographies in this Monograph contain more than 1000 different references and the names of more than 600 authors.

ACKNOWLEDGEMENTS

"Car enfin non omnia possumus omnes, & un homme seul ne peut parcourir tous les Pais & toutes les Bibliotheques, ny lire tous les Livres, ny puiser par consequent dans toutes les sources qui luy pourroient faciliter ce travail."

This was written by S. de Brossard in the introduction of the third part of the second edition of **Dictionaire de Musique** which appeared in 1705. In this introduction of **Catalogue des Auteurs** Brossard explains that he wanted to give a detailed bibliography containing work and names of authors *"qui ont écrit touchant la Musique"*. However: *"Mais il faut que je l'avoue, malgré tout mon travail; mes Memoires ne suffisent pas pour executer avec l'exactitude que je souhaitterois, un projet de cette nature."*

Therefore Brossard confines himself to the listing of three categories of names of authors without giving further references. These categories, summarizing ten years of work and containing about 230, 100 and 600 names, respectively, are composed as follows.

"Dans la premiere on trouvera les Noms des Auteurs que j'ay vus, lus & examinez moy-meme.
Dans la 2e, on trouvera les Noms de ceux que je n'ay pas encor eu le temps, ny l'occasion de lire & d'examiner, mais qui sont aisez a trouver, & que j'espere de lire avec le temps.
Dans la 3e, enfin on trouvera les Noms de ceux que je n'ay point lus, ny vus, & que je connois que par les yeux, & sur la foy d'autruy."

After spending only a few months on the compilation of this Monograph, with the help of review and abstract journals and with the help of modern tools which make it possible to store, change and format extensive lists of publications it is almost impudent to do so, but I wish to dedicate this Monograph to S. de Brossard.

Several approaches to the parsing problem fall outside the scope of the present Monograph. Hopefully I will have the opportunity to edit a more complete version of this Monograph in the future. A number of people have contributed to this Monograph in various ways. Peter Kugel gave me permission to use his poem "Trees". Without Adri Breukink Brossard would have been unknown to me. Many years ago Leo Verbeek introduced me to the parsing problem. Jaco de Bakker gave me the opportunity to spend some years on research in topics related with parsing. Michael Harrison and Derick Wood were among those who gave me feedback at several occasions. I gratefully acknowledge the help of those who contributed to earlier versions of parts of these bibliographies. Hans Meijer and Rinus Plasmeijer gave some help with the phototypesetter. Finally, I thank the Informatics Department of the Katholieke Universiteit Nijmegen in the Netherlands for providing me with the necessary opportunities and facilities which made this Monograph possible. The Monograph has been completed at the Computer Science Department of Twente University of Technology in Enschede.

REFERENCES

1. J.W. Backus. The syntax and semantics of the proposed international algebraic language of the Zurich ACM-GAMM Conference. Proc. *Int. Conf. on Inform. Processing,* UNESCO Paris, 1959, 125-132.

2. F.L. Bauer. Historical remarks on compiler construction. In: *Compiler Construction: An Advanced Course.* F.L. Bauer and J. Eickel (eds.), Lect. Notes in Comp. Sci. 21, Springer-Verlag, Berlin, 1974, 603-621.

3. S. de Brossard. *Dictionaire de Musique.* Seconde Edition, Christophe Baliard, seul Imprimeur du Roy pour la Musique, rue S. Jean de Beauvais, au Mont-Parnasse, Paris, MDCCV.

4. N. Chomsky. Three models for the description of language. *IRE Trans. on Information Theory,* IT-2 (1956), 113-124.

5. R.W. Floyd. On the nonexistence of a phrase structure grammar for ALGOL 60. *Comm. ACM* 5 (1962), 483-484.

6. S.A. Greibach. Formal languages: Origins and directions. In: 20th Annual Symposium on *Foundations of Computer Science,* 1979, 66-90.

7. D.E. Knuth. Semantics of context-free languages. *Math. Systems Theory* 2 (1968), 127-145.

8. C.H.A. Koster. Affix grammars. In: *ALGOL 68 Implementation.* J.E. Peck (ed.), North-Holland Publ. Co., Amsterdam, 1971, 95-109.

9. F.C.N. Pereira and D.H.D. Warren. Definite clause grammars for language analysis - A survey of the formalism and a comparison with augmented transition networks. *Artificial Intelligence* 13 (1980), 231-278.

10. K.-J. Raiha. Bibliography on attribute grammars. *SIGPLAN Notices* 15, Nr.3, March 1980, 35-44.

11. P. Wegner. Programming languages: The first 25 years. *IEEE Trans. on Computers,* Vol. C-25 (1976), 1207-1225.

12. A. van Wijngaarden (ed.). *(Revised) Report on the Algorithmic Language ALGOL 68.* 1968, revised: 1972.

2. TOP-DOWN PARSING: A BIBLIOGRAPHY

SURVEY OF THE LITERATURE

2.1. General and History

This bibliography contains references to reports and papers on (deterministic) top-down parsing, recursive descent and LL(k) grammars and languages. In 1978 Wood[400] compiled a bibliography on 'top-down deterministic parsing'. In this bibliography we give a more recent and more complete survey of papers and reports on top-down deterministic parsing. Many, but not all the references of [400] have been included. Some of the papers not included are mentioned in other recent bibliographies which deal with other approaches of the parsing problem for context-free grammars and languages. These other bibliographies are on:

- LR-grammars and parsing (see Section 3 of this Monograph and Burgess and James[60])

- precedence relations (see Section 4 of this Monograph and Nijholt[264])

- error handling (Ciesinger[69])

- translator writing tools (Meijer and Nijholt[237])

LL(k) grammars were introduced by Lewis and Stearns[217,218]. However, in [217] they used the name TD(k) grammar (Top Down grammar). The name (parsing from Left to right using Leftmost derivations and k symbols of lookahead) was introduced by Knuth[181], and most of their formal properties were first discussed by Rosenkrantz and Stearns[306]. Independently, Wood[396], building on earlier work in Great Britain, and Thompson and Booth[357] introduced similar classes of grammars.

Long before the formal introduction of LL(k) grammars parsing methods suitable for LL-type grammars have been used in compilers and compiler writing systems. One of these methods has become known as recursive descent, a method which can also be considered as parsing with restricted transition diagrams (cf. Conway[77]) and restricted parsing machines (cf. Knuth[181]). Recursive descent parsing is sometimes attributed to Lucas[227]. In that case the parser consists of a set of recursive procedures which recognize the input. LL(k) parsing is also known as predictive parsing. In that case the implementation of the parser uses a table and a pushdown stack. In fact, the formal and explicit introduction of the pushdown stack in mathematical linguistics was motivated by this predictive parsing method. In 1961 Oettinger[272] explains that the method grew out of reflections on a technique used by I. Rhodes in automatic translation of natural languages. The following explanation is from Oettinger's paper. *"The Rhodes method of "predictive" syntactic analysis is based on the observation that in scanning through a Russian sentence from left to right it is possible, on the one hand, to make predictions about the syntactic structures to be met further to the right and, on the other hand, to determine the syntactic role of the word currently being scanned by testing what previously made predictions it fulfills. The predictions are stored in a linear array called the "prediction pool" which behaves approximately as a pushdown store. Before a new sentence is scanned, a set of initial predictions is entered in the pool. The first word of the sentence is then admitted, and a test is made to see if the topmost prediction in the pool will accept it. If so, the successful prediction is erased from the prediction pool, and new predictions based both on lexical data about the word from a dictionary and on syntactic rules embodied in the predictive analysis system are entered into the prediction pool on top of whatever earlier predictions may have remained there. The system is then ready to process the next word in the sentence."* In Bauer[28] other remarks can be found on parsing methods in the early years of compiler construction.

2.2. Properties of Grammars and Languages

Programming languages are not necessarily LL(k) languages. In fact, some simple constructs in wellknown programming languages can not be described by any LL(k) grammar. However, in the practice of compiler writing such a problem can almost always easily be handled. It is decidable whether, for a fixed k, a context-free grammar is LL(k). Moreover, there exist methods to investigate whether a given language is not LL(k) (cf. Beatty[30,32]). For any two LL(k) grammars it is decidable whether they are equivalent, i.e., whether they generate the same language. This was first shown by Rosenkrantz and Stearns[308] using automata theory. This pushdown automata approach has been the start of extensive research activities to solve the equivalence problem for deterministic languages. Korenjak and Hopcroft[187] have used a more direct scheme (based on grammars) to solve the problem for a simple subclass of the LL grammars. See also Wood[399] and Butzbach[63]. Attempts have been made to generalize this direct scheme such that it can be used for the equivalence problem of LL(k) grammars. See Harrison, Havel and Yehudai[133], Olshansky and Pnueli[270] and Tomita[360,361].

LL(k) grammars are properly included in the class of LR(k) grammars. The LL(k) languages are properly included in the family of deterministic or LR(1) languages. There exists an infinite hierarchy of LL(k) languages based on the look-ahead k (Kurki-Suonio[206]).

From the point of view of parsing LL(1) grammars are very attractive. Software has been developed to transform grammars into LL(1) type grammars. A successful example is SID (Syntax Improving Device) (see Foster[99]), but also in more recently constructed compiler writing systems transformations are performed to obtain a grammar which is more suitable for the system. Such transformations include left factoring, elimination of left recursion, transformations to Greibach normal form and some others. These transformations should be done in such a way that the original *semantics* of the language can be preserved. A survey of research in this area can be found in Nijholt[255]. For existing programming languages (e.g. FORTRAN, ALGOL 60, ALGOL 68, PASCAL and ADA) grammars have been designed which can be used by top-down parsing methods.

2.3. Parsing and Error-Handling

LL(k) parsing can be done in linear time. In Hunt, Szymanski and Ullman[149] a lower bound for LL(k) testing is indirectly obtained from testing the LR(k) property. More recently, Sippu and Soisalon-Soininen[332] have obtained a faster algorithm for LL(k) testing. There exist algorithms which perform the test for subclasses of the LL(k) grammars. E.g., for k = 1 (Johnson and Sethi[168,169]) and for strong LL(k) grammars (Hunt, Szymanski and Ullman[155]).

Apart from the references to papers and reports with theoretical results on LL(k) grammars, parsing and languages, references can be found to publications which deal with error handling and with the construction of parsers (or compilers) and parser generating systems (or compiler writing systems) in which essential use is made of properties of LL(k) grammars and parsing. Irons[164] describes one of the first top-down error recovery mechanisms. Since then, interest in formal methods which can be used in the automatic generation of error correcting parsers has rapidly increased. In Burgess[59] it is shown, among others, how top-down parsers for Wood's *left factored* grammars can recover from errors. Wirth[391] discusses error handling in a top-down PL/0 parser. Lewi et al[215] and Milton, Kirchhoff and Rowland[240] describe LL parser generators with error recovery and error correcting mechanisms. Fischer, Milton and Quiring[96] have introduced an *insertion-only* LL error-corrector which can be used for those LL(1) grammars for which errors can be repaired by a suitable insertion of a terminal string. LL(k) parsers can be constructed such that they have the property that each erroneous input symbol will be immediately detected. This is not the case for strong LL parsers. However, each LL(1) grammar can be modified such that its strong LL parser has this *Immediate Error Detection* property (cf. Fischer, Tai and Milton[94]). Other correction techniques for LL parsers can be found in, among others, Amman[9], Seeger[321], Pai[273], Pai and Kieburz[275] and Roehrich[302]. In Backhouse[18] a simple recovery scheme is implemented in a recursive descent parser for PL/0.

2.4. More General Than Context-Free

By allowing backtracking top-down parsing methods can be made to work for every context-free language. However, such a method will be exponential in time complexity. Whenever a grammar is not LL(1) then there is still the possibility to use an LL(1) parsing method. For example, methods in Aho, Johnson and Ullman[3] and Wharton[386] make it possible to parse ambiguous grammars. Moreover, in a compiler writing system attempts can be made to modify the input grammar.

It is also possible to consider more general classes of grammars and languages and use a generalization of the LL parsing method. This has been done for certain subclasses of the context-sensitive grammars. See e.g. Barth[27] and Szabo[349]. Special methods have been developed for indexed grammars (Sebesta and Jones [320], Parchmann, Duske and Specht[277,278] and Weiss[382]) and for macro grammars (Heydthausen and Mehlhorn[135] and Mehlhorn[235]). Parsing attribute grammars can be done in such a way that evaluating the attributes can influence the parsing. See Lewis, Rosenkrantz and Stearns[220] for the general theory of deterministic attributed translation. LL parsing and evaluation of attribute grammars is discussed in Madsen[229], Madsen and Jones[228], Milton[239], Milton and Fischer[241], Raiha and Ukkonen[296], Rowland[311] and Wilhelm[389]. Top-down parsing of two-level (van Wijngaarden) grammars has been discussed in, e.g., Barringer[24], Hunter et al[161] (see also Meijer[236]) and Meertens and van Vliet[234].

Instead of using a fixed amount k of look-ahead it is also possible to perform LL parsing with *regular look-ahead*. In this way LL-regular grammars have been obtained (Jarzabek and Krawczyk[167] and Nijholt[256]). In Poplawski[287] this class is further generalized in order to include ambiguous grammars which can be parsed using disambiguating rules. The equivalence problem for LL-regular grammars is decidable (Nijholt[260]).

2.5. Compilers and Compiler Writing Systems

Lewis and Rosenkrantz[219] first used LL theory and automata theory to develop an ALGOL compiler. See also the compiler described in Wirth[390] and the generating systems in Rosen[303], Ward[376], Lewi et al[214], Hunter et al[161], Milton et al[240], Pyster[293], Shyamasundar[328], Wilhelm et al[388] and Aronson and Laforce[15].

REFERENCES

1. P.W. Abrahams. Syntax directed parser for recalcitrant grammars. *Int. J. Computer Math.* 3 (1972), 105-116.

2. A.V. Aho and J.D. Ullman. *The Theory of Parsing, Translation, and Compiling.* Vols. 1 and 2. Prentice Hall, Englewood Cliffs, N.J., 1972 and 1973.

3. A.V. Aho, S.C. Johnson and J.D. Ullman. Deterministic parsing of ambiguous grammars. *Comm. ACM* 18 (1975), 441-452.

4. A.V. Aho and J.D. Ullman. *Principles of Compiler Design.* Addison-Wesley, Reading, Mass., 1977.

5. U. Amman. The method of structured programming applied to the development of a compiler. In: *Intern. Computing Symposium 1973,* A. Gunther et al (eds.), North-Holland Publ. Co., Amsterdam, 1974, 93-99.

6. U. Amman. Error recovery in recursive descent parsers. Inst. fuer Informatik der ETH, ETH-Zentrum, Zuerich.

7. U. Amman. Die Entwicklung eines PASCAL-Compilers nach der Methode des strukturierten Programmierens. Dissertation, ETH, Zuerich.

8. U. Amman. Error recovery in recursive descent parsers and run-time storage organization. Report nr.25, Institut fuer Informatik der ETH, Zuerich, 1978.

9. U. Amman. Summary on error recovery in recursive descent parsers. Prel. Doc. (Vol.2) of: *State of the Art and Future Trends in Compilation.* Montpellier, 1978, 231-238.

10. S.O. Anderson. Eliminating left recursion in attribute grammars. Manuscript, Dept. of Computer Science, Heriot-Watt University, Edinburgh, 1978.

11. S.O. Anderson and R.C. Backhouse. Locally least-error recovery in Earley's algorithm. *ACM Trans. Progr. Lang. Syst.* 3 (1981), 318-347.

12. A.V. Anisimov. Top-down analysis of programming languages without backtracking (in Russian). Proc. 2nd Symp. on *Mathematical Foundations of Computer Science,* 1973, High Tatras, Czechoslovakia, 175-180.

13. A.V. Anisimov. Formal grammars that take into account external terminal contexts (Russian). *Kibernetika* (Kiev) 1974, No.3, 81-88.

14. J. Aoe, Y. Yamamoto and R. Shimada. A method for constructing LL(1) parsing tables. *Trans. Inst. Electron. & Comm. Eng. Jpn.* (Japan), Vol.E61, No.12, p.1008, Dec. 1978.

15. M. Aronson and D.S. Laforce. COG User's guide. TR 81-8, Computer Science Department, SUNY, Albany, 1981.

16. P. Bachman. Die Lokalisierung syntaktischer Fehler in kontextfreien Sprachen. *Elektronische Informationsverarbeitung und Kybernetik (EIK)* 9 (1973), 341-353.

17. S. Backes. Top-down syntax analysis and Floyd-Evans production language. Proc. of *IFIP Congress 71*, North-Holland Publ. Co., Amsterdam, 1972, 504-508.

18. R.C. Backhouse. *Syntax of Programming Languages: Theory and Practice.* Prentice Hall International, London, 1979.

19. R.C. Backhouse and S.O. Anderson. Least cost repair of syntax errors. *EATCS-Bulletin* 7, February 1979, 10-14.

20. R. Banerji. Some studies in syntax-directed parsing. In: *Computation in Linguistics.* P. Garvin (ed.), Indiana University Press, 1966, 76-123.

21. M.P. Barnett and R.P. Futrelle. Syntactic analysis by digital computer. *Comm. ACM* 5 (1962), 515-526.

22. W.A. Barrett and J.D. Couch. *Compiler Construction: Theory and Practice.* Science Research Associates, Inc., 1979.

23. H. Barringer and C.H. Lindsey. The Manchester ALGOL 68 compiler (Part 1). Proc. of the 5th Annual III Conf., *Implementation and Design of Algorithmic Languages.* J. Andre and J.-P. Banatre (eds.), 1977, 145-165.

24. H. Barringer. Parsing and error recovery in ALGOL 68. Ph.D. Thesis, University of Manchester, 1978.

25. G. Barth. Protokollgrammatiken - Ein Konzept zur zeitvarianten Kontrolle bei kontextfreien Ersetzungen. Dissertation, Fachbereich Informatik, Universitaet Kaiserslautern, 1977.

26. G. Barth. Efficient non-context-free parsing. Rep.#17, 1977, Fachbereich Informatik, Universitaet Karlsruhe, Also: In: *GI-7.Jahrestagung,* H.-J. Schneider (ed.), Informatik Fachberichte 10, Springer-Verlag, Berlin, 1977, 1-15.

27. G. Barth. Fast recognition of context-sensitive structures. *Computing* 22 (1979), 243-256.

28. F.L. Bauer. Historical remarks on compiler construction. In: *Compiler Construction: An Advanced Course,* F.L. Bauer and J. Eickel (eds.), Lect. Notes in Comp. Sci. 21, Springer-Verlag, Berlin, 1974, 603-621.

29. J.C. Beatty. Iteration theorems for LL(k) languages. Proc. of the Ninth Annual Symp. on *Theory of Computing,* 1977, 122-131.

30. J.C. Beatty. Iteration theorems for the LL(k) languages. Ph.D. Thesis, Lawrence Livermore Laboratory, University of California, Livermore, 1977.

31. J.C. Beatty. On the relationship between the LL(1) and LR(1) grammars. Res. Report CS-79-36, University of Waterloo, Waterloo, Ontario.

32. J.C. Beatty. Two iteration theorems for the LL(k) languages. *Theoret. Comput. Sci.* 12 (1980), 193-228.

33. M.I. Beljakov and L.G. Natanson. A modification of top-down parsing. *Programmirovanie* 1979, No.5, 50-55, 80 (Russian); translated as *Program. Comput. Software* 5 (1979), No.5, 335-339 (1980).

34. A. Birman and J.D. Ullman. Parsing algorithms with backtrack. Conf. Record of 11th Annual Symp. on *Switching and Automata Theory,* 1970, 153-174.

35. A. Boccalatte, M. Di Manzo and D. Sciarra. Error recovery with attribute grammars. *Computer Journal* 25 (1982), 331-337.

36. G.V. Bochmann and P. Ward. Compiler writing system for attribute grammars. Publ.#199, Dept. d'Informatique, Univ. de Montreal.

37. G.V. Bochmann and P. Ward. Simple scheme for syntactic error recovery in LL(1) analysis. Publ.#xx, Dept. d'Informatique, Univ. de Montreal, 1975.

38. H. Bock. Programmierersyntax - Eine neue syntakt. Beschreibung von Programmiersprachen. Techn. Bericht HE/FI-UL Nr.40/71.

39.   H. Bock and B. Schinzel. Strukturtreue Syntaxkompression und zugehoerige Parserprozeduren. In: *Zweite Fachtagung ueber Programmiersprachen*. GI-Bericht Nr.4, Gesellschaft fuer Mathematik und Datenverarbeitung, 1972, 141-163.

40.   H. Bock. Error-recovery in prozedurorientierter Syntaxanalyse. German Chapter of the ACM, Lectures I/II-1973 (Fachtagung ueber Behandlung von Syntaxfehlern in Compilern), 107-144.

41.   R. Bonet, A. Kung, K. Ripke, R.K. Yates, M. Sommer and J. Winkler. ADA syntax diagrams for top-down analysis. *SIGPLAN Notices* 16, Nr.3, March 1981, 29-41.

42.   E. Book, D.V. Schorre and S.J. Sherman. CWIC User's guide: General description. System Development Corporation, TM-L-4185/001/00, May 14, 1969.

43.   E. Book, D.V. Schorre and S.J. Sherman. CWIC User's guide: The syntax language. System Development Corporation, TM-L-4185/002/01, June 19, 1969.

44.   J. Bordier. Elimination de la recursivite a gauche dans une grammaire context-free. *Revue Francaise d'Informatique et de Recherche Operationelle*, B-3, 4 (1970), 145-163.

45.   J. Bordier. Methodes pour la mise au point de grammaires LL(1). These 3.cycle, Grenoble, 1971.

46.   J. Bordier and H. Saya. A necessary and sufficient condition for a power language to be LL(k). *Computer Journal* 16 (1973), 351-356.

47.   R. Bornat. *Understanding and Writing Compilers*. MacMillan and Co., Ltd., London, 1979.

48.   M. Bouckaert, A. Pirotte and M. Snelling. Improvements to Earley's context-free parser. In: *GI-3.Jahrestagung*, W. Brauer (ed.), Lect. Notes in Comp. Sci. 1, Springer-Verlag, Berlin, 1973, 104-112.

49.   R.A. Brooker and D. Morris. A description of Mercury Autocode in terms of a phrase structure language. *Ann. Reviews Aut. Programming* 2 (1961), 29-66.

50.   R.A. Brooker and D. Morris. A general translation program for phrase structure languages. *J. Assoc. Comput. Mach.* 9 (1962), 1-10.

51. R.A. Brooker and D. Morris. The compiler-compiler. *Ann. Reviews Aut. Programming* 3 (1963), 229-275.

52. R.A. Brooker, D. Morris and J.S. Rohl. Experience with the compiler-compiler. *Computer Journal* 9 (1967), p.350.

53. R.A. Brooker. Top-to-bottom parsing rehabilitated? *Comm. ACM* 10 (1967), 223-224.

54. B.M. Brosgol. Deterministic translation grammars. Proc. 8th Annual Princeton Conf. on *Information Sciences and Systems,* 1974, 300-306.

55. B.M. Brosgol. Deterministic translation grammars. Ph.D. Thesis, TR-74, Harvard University, Cambridge, Mass., 1974.

56. B.M. Brosgol. A bottom-up approach to top-down parsing. Proc. of the 1977 Conf. on *Information Sciences and Systems.* The John Hopkins University, 1977, 195-201.

57. S. Buerger, E. Diedrich and G.F. Schrack. Entwicklung eines Praeprozessors fuer die in PASCAL eingebettete Graphik-Sprache LIG/P mit hilfe eines Compiler-Compiler. In: *Compiler-Compiler.* W. Henhapl (ed.), 3. GI-Fachgespraech, Muenchen, March 1982, 120-152.

58. C.J. Burgess. Error diagnostics in syntax-directed compilers. Ph.D. Thesis, University of Bristol, 1971.

59. C.J. Burgess. Compile-time error diagnostics in syntax-directed compilers. *Computer Journal* 15 (1972), 302-307.

60. C. Burgess and L. James. An indexed bibliography for LR grammars and parsers. *SIGPLAN Notices* 16, Nr.8, August 1981, 14-26.

61. M. Burke and G.A. Fisher Jr. A practical method for syntactic error diagnosis and recovery. Proc. of the SIGPLAN'82 Symp. on *Compiler Construction,* 1982, 67-78.

62. P. Butzbach. Sur l'equivalence des grammaires simple. Langages algebriques (Proc. First meeting, Information Theory, Bonascre, 1973), 223-245. Ecole Nat. Sup. Tech. Avancees, Paris, 1978.

63. P. Butzbach. Une famille de congruence de Thue pour lesquelles le problem de l'equivalence est decidable. Application a l'equivalence des grammaires separees. In: *Automata, Languages and Programming*, M. Nivat (ed.), North-Holland Publ. Co., Amsterdam, 1973, 377-390.

64. B.A. Chartres and J.J. Florentin. A universal syntax-directed top-down analyzer. *J. Assoc. Comput. Mach.* 15 (1968), 447-464.

65. T.E. Cheatham and K. Sattley. Syntax directed compilation. Proc. *AFIPS Spring Joint Computer Conf.*, Vol.25, 1964, p.31.

66. C.C. Chen. A new method to handle the left-recursions for top-down parsing in compiler design. In: *System Modeling and Optimization*. R.F. Drenick and F. Kozin (eds.), Proc. of the 10th IFIP Conference 1981, Lect. Notes in Control and Information Sciences, Springer-Verlag, Berlin, 1982, 888-891.

67. Y.E. Cho. Simple left corner grammars. Seventh Annual Princeton Conf. on *Information Sciences and Systems*, 1973, 557-557.

68. J. Ciesinger. Generating error recovery in a compiler generating system. In: *Programmiersprachen*, H.J. Schneider and M. Nagl (eds.), GI-4.Fachtagung, Informatik Fachberichte 1, Springer-Verlag, Berlin, 1976, 185-193.

69. J. Ciesinger. A bibliography of error-handling. *SIGPLAN Notices* 14, Nr.1, January 1979, 16-26.

70. J. Ciesinger. Discussion of some error correction techniques. In: *GI-9.Jahrestagung*, K.H. Boehling (eds.), Informatik Fachberichte 19, Springer-Verlag, Berlin, 1979, 252-261.

71. J. Ciesinger. Discussion of some error correction techniques. Technical Report, Technische Universitaet Muenchen, Inst. fuer Informatik, 1979.

72. COGENT Compiler generator user's guide. Virtual Systems, Inc., 1976.

73. D.J. Cohen and C.C. Gotlieb. A list structure form of grammars for syntactic analysis. *Computing Surveys* 2 (1970), 65-82.

74. J. Cohen and R. Sitver. A case study in program transformation: translation into Polish. *IEEE Trans. Softw. Eng.*, SE-5, 6 (1979), 575-586.

75. J. Cohen, R. Sitver and D. Auty. Evaluating and improving recursive descent parsers. *IEEE Trans. Softw. Eng.*, SE-5, 5 (1979), 593-606.

76. J.D. Cointment III. CCC - A mixed strategy compiler-compiler. Ph.D. Thesis, Southern Methodist University, Dallas, Texas, May 1972.

77. M.E. Conway. Design of a separable transition-diagram compiler. *Comm. ACM* 6 (1963), 396-408.

78. B. Courcelle. Une forme canonique pour les grammaires simple deterministes. *Revue Francaise d'Informatique et de Recherche Operationelle*, R-1, 1974, 19-36.

79. K. Culik II. Contribution to deterministic top-down analysis of context-free languages. *Kybernetika* (Prague) 4 (1968), 422-431.

80. O.-J. Dahl. Top-down parsers expressed in a high level language. Lecture Notes Series No.8, Institute of Mathematics, University of Oslo, 1973.

81. A.J. Demers. Generalized left corner parsing. Conf. Record of the 4th ACM Symp. on *Principles of Programming Languages*, 1977, 170-182.

82. J. Demner and J. Kral. On the distinction between LL(k) and strong LL(k) grammars. Unpublished note, 1975.

83. J. Demner and J. Kral. How strong are the strong LL(k) grammars? Collection of papers, Technical University of Prague, UVT-2/75/M, 1975.

84. P. Deussen. Nine classes of parsable languages obtained by refining one abstract accepting algorithm. Int. Bericht 1978/1. Inst. fuer Informatik, Universitaet Karlsruhe.

85. P. Deussen. Strategies in acceptors and their relation to LR(k)-/LL(k)-theories. Report Nr. 8/77, Inst. fuer Informatik, Universitaet Karlsruhe, 1977.

86. P. Deussen. A unified approach to the generation and the acceptance of formal languages. *Acta Informatica* 9 (1978), 377-390.

87. P. Deussen. One abstract parsing algorithm for all kinds of parsers. In: *Automata, Languages and Programming*, H.A. Maurer (ed.), Lect. Notes in Comp. Sci. 71, Springer-Verlag, Berlin, 1979, 203-217.

88. A.G. Duncan and J.S. Hutchison. Using attribute grammars to test designs and implementations. 5th Int. Conf. on *Software Engineering*, 1981 (San Diego), 170-178.

89. J. Earley. Ambiguity and precedence in syntax description. *Acta Informatica* 4 (1975), 183-192.

90. N. El Djabri. Reducing the size of LL(1) parsing tables. TR-119, Dept. of EECS, Princeton Univ., Princeton, N.J., 1973.

91. J. Feldman and D. Gries. Translator writing systems. *Comm. ACM* 11 (1968), 77-113.

92. H. Feuerhahn. A binary control structure and its relationship to grammars and side effects. In: *GI-4.Jahrestagung,* D. Siefkes (ed.), Lect. Notes in Comp. Sci. 26, Springer-Verlag, Berlin, 1974, 224-232.

93. C.N. Fischer, D.R. Milton and S.B. Quiring. An efficient insertion only error corrector for LL(1) parsers. Conf. Record of the Fourth ACM Symp. on *Principles of Programming Languages,* 1977, 97-103.

94. C.N. Fischer, K.C. Tai and D.R. Milton. Immediate error detection in strong LL(1) parsers. *Information Processing Letters* 8 (1979), 261-266.

95. C.N. Fischer and B.A. Dion. On testing for insert-correctability in context-free grammars. University of Wisconsin-Madison, Tech. Report 355.

96. C.N. Fischer, D.R. Milton and S.B. Quiring. Efficient LL(1) error correction and recovery using only insertions. *Acta Informatica* 13 (1980), 141-154.

97. C.N. Fischer, J. Mauney and D.R. Milton. A locally least-cost LL(1) error corrector. Tech. Rep.371, Computer Sciences Dept., University of Wisconsin-Madison, 1979.

98. R.W. Floyd. The syntax of programming languages - a survey. *IEEE Trans. on Electr. Computers,* Vol.EC-13, 1964, 346-353.

99. J.M. Foster. A syntax improving program. R.R.E. Memorandum 2389, July 1967. Also: *Computer Journal* 11 (1968), 31-34.

100. J.M. Foster. *Automatic Syntactic Analysis.* Computer Monographs No.7, American Elsevier, New York, 1970.

101. E. Foxley and P. King. A meta-semantic language for use with top-down syntax analyzer. *Information Processing 68,* Proc. IFIP Congress, Vol.1, 1969, 366-372.

102. M. Frentiu. A global top-down error correcting parser. *Mathematica* (Cluj) 19 (42) (1977), No.1, 41-43 (1978).

103. D. Friede. Ueber deterministische kontextfreie Sprachen und rekursiven Abstieg. VI/78, IFI Berichte, Universitaet Hamburg, 1978.

104. D. Friede. Transition diagrams and strict deterministic grammars. Proc. 4th *GI-Conf. Theoretical Computer Science*, K. Weihrauch (ed.), Lect. Notes in Comp. Sci. 67, Springer-Verlag, Berlin, 1979, 113-123.

105. D. Friede. Partitioned LL(k) grammars. In: *Automata, Languages and Programming*, H.A. Maurer (ed.), Lect. Notes in Comp. Sci. 71, Springer-Verlag, Berlin, 1979, 245-255.

106. D. Friede. Partitioned context-free grammars. TUM I8115, Technische Universitaet Muenchen, Institut fuer Informatik, 1981.

107. D. Friede. On partitioned van Wijngaarden grammars. TUM I8207, June 1982, Institut fuer Informatik, Technische Universitaet Muenchen.

108. E.P. Friedman. The inclusion problem for simple languages. *Theoret. Comput. Sci.* 1 (1975), 297-316.

109. M.M. Geller, H.B. Hunt III, T.G. Szymanski and J.D. Ullman. Economy of description by parsers, dpda's and pda's. *Theoret. Comput. Sci.* 4 (1977), 143-159.

110. L. Gerevich. Syntax-parser of W-grammars (in Russian). *Szam. Automatiz. Kutato Intezete*, Kozlemenyek, 21 (1978), 7-26.

111. L.J.M. Geurts and L.G.T.L. Meertens. Keyword grammars. Report IW86/77, Mathematisch Centrum, Amsterdam, 1977.

112. L.J.M. Geurts and L.G.T.L. Meertens. Keyword grammars. Proc. of the 5th Annual III Conf. *Implementation and Design of Algorithmic Languages*. J. Andre and J.-P. Banatre (eds.), 1977, 1-12.

113. C. Ghezzi. LL(1) grammars supporting an efficient error handling. *Information Processing Letters* 3 (1975), 174-176.

114. C. Ghezzi. Automatic recovery and correction of syntactic errors in top-down compilers. *J. Cybernet.* 5 (1975), No.3, 31-41 (1976).

115. R. Giegerich and R. Wilhelm. Implementierbarkeit attributierter grammati-ken. In: *GI-7.Jahrestagung,* H.J. Schneider (ed.), Informatik Fachberichte 10, Springer-Verlag, Berlin, 1977, 17-36.

116. A.E. Glennie. On the syntax machine and the construction of a universal compiler. Carnegie Tech. Computation Centre Report, No.2, July 1960.

117. V.N. Glushkova. On the simplification of LL(k) grammars (in Russian). *Programmirovanie* 11 (1975), Nr.6, 880-890 (1976).

118. V.N. Glushkova. Towards a simplification of LL(k) grammars. *Program. Comput. Software* 3 (1977), 266-273.

119. V.N. Glushkova. Lexical analysis of LL(k) languages. *Program. Comput. Software* 5 (1979), 166-172.

120. N.G. Grafeeva. A class of grammars which allow parsing with backtracking by Unger's method. *Program. Comput. Software* 7, No.2, March-April 1981, 86-90.

121. S.A. Greibach. Formal parsing systems. *Comm. ACM* 7 (1964), 499-504.

122. S.A. Greibach. A new normal-form theorem for context-free phrase structure grammars. *J. Assoc. Comput. Mach.* 12 (1965), 42-52.

123. S.A. Greibach. A simple proof of the standard form theorem for context-free grammars. Report No. NSF-18, Harvard University, 1976.

124. S.A. Greibach. Comments on the roots of theorems and languages, both easy and hard. *SIGACT News,* Vol.13, Winter 1981, No.1, 26-29.

125. M. Griffiths. Analyse deterministe et compilateurs. Thesis for Docteur d'etat, University of Grenoble, 1969.

126. M. Griffiths and M. Peltier. Grammar transformation as an aid to compiler production. Manuscript, undated.

127. T.V. Griffiths and S.R. Petrick. On the relative efficiencies of context-free grammar recognizers. *Comm. ACM* 8 (1965), 289-300.

128. T.V. Griffiths and S.R. Petrick. Top-down versus bottom-up analysis. *IFIP Congress 68,* Software I, Booklet B, 80-85.

129. M. Griffiths. LL(1) grammars and analyzers. In: *Compiler Construction: An Advanced Course,* F.L. Bauer and J. Eickel (eds.), Lect. Notes in Comp. Sci. 21, Springer-Verlag, Berlin, 1974, 55-84.

130. M. Griffiths. Toute grammaire LL(k) est LR(k). *RAIRO Informatique Theorique* 8 (1974), 55-58.

131. M. Hammer. A new grammatical transformation into deterministic top-down form. Mac TR-119, Ph.D. Thesis, Massachusetts Institute of Technology, 1974.

132. M. Hammer. A new grammatical transformation into LL(k) form. Proc. of the Sixth Annual ACM Symp. on *Theory of Computing,* 1974, 266-275.

133. M.A. Harrison, I.M. Havel and A. Yehudai. An equivalence of grammars through transformation trees. *Theoret. Comput. Sci.* 9 (1979), 173-206.

134. M. Heydthausen and K. Mehlhorn. Top-down parsing of macro grammars. Rep. A76-03, Universitaet des Saarlandes, Saarbruecken, 1976.

135. M. Heydthausen and K. Mehlhorn. Top-down parsing of macro grammars. *GI-6.Jahrestagung,* E.J. Neuhold (ed.), Informatik Fachberichte 5, Springer-Verlag, Berlin, 1976, 95-108.

136. S. Heilbrunner. Using item grammars to prove LR(k) theorems. Bericht Nr. 7701, Hochschule der Bundeswehr, Muenchen, Fachbereich Informatik, 1977.

137. S. Heilbrunner. Definition, analysis and transformation of LC(k) grammars. Bericht Nr. 7802, Fachbereich Informatik, Hochschule der Bundeswehr, Muenchen, 1978.

138. S. Heilbrunner. On the definition of ELR(k) and ELL(k) grammars. *Acta Informatica* 11 (1979), 169-176.

139. S. Heilbrunner. Zerteilungsverfahren mit unbeschraenkter Vorschau. Bericht Nr.8005, Fachbereich Informatik, Hochschule der Bundeswehr, Muenchen, 1980.

140. S. Heilbrunner. A metatheorem for undecidable properties of formal languages and its applications to LRR and LLR grammars and languages. Manuscript, Fachbereich Informatik, Hochschule der Bundeswehr, Muenchen, April 1981.

141. S. Heilbrunner. Tests for the LR-, LL-, and LC-regular conditions. Manuscript, Fachbereich Informatik, Hochschule der Bundeswehr, Muenchen, April 1981.

142. S. Heilbrunner. A parsing automata approach to LR theory. *Theoret. Comput. Sci.* 15 (1981), 117-157.

143. L.E. Heindel and J.T. Roberto. *LANG-PAK - An Interactive Language Design System.* American Elsevier Publ. Co., New York, 1975.

144. R. Herrmann. Ein Program zur Untersuchung von Analysierbarkeitseigenschaften fuer Top-Down-Verfahren. Diplomarbeit, Inst. fuer Informatik, Universitaet Muenchen, 1976.

145. F.R.A. Hopgood. *Compiling Techniques.* Computer Monographs No.8, American Elsevier, New York, 1969.

146. G.T. Hochgesang. An algorithm for grammatical inference of programming languages. Ph.D. Thesis, Purdue University, Lafayette, Ind., June 1972.

147. G. Hotz. LL(k)- und LR(k)- Invarianz von kontextfreien Grammatiken unter einer Transformation auf Greibachnormalform. Fachbereich Informatik, Univ. des Saarlandes, Saarbruecken, 1978.

148. G. Hotz and R.J. Ross. LL(k)- und LR(k)- Invarianz von kontextfreien Grammatiken unter einer Transformation auf Greibach-Normalform. *Elektronische Informationsverarbeitung und Kybernetik (EIK)* 15 (1979), 73-86.

149. H.B. Hunt III, T.G. Szymanski and J.D. Ullman. On the complexity of LR(k) testing. *Comm. ACM* 18 (1975), 707-716.

150. H.B. Hunt III and T.G. Szymanski. Lower bounds and reductions between grammar problems. Techn. Report 216, Princeton University, August 1976.

151. H.B. Hunt III and T.G. Szymanski. Complexity metatheorems for context-free grammar problems. *J. Comput. System Sci.* 13 (1976), 318-334.

152. H.B. Hunt and T.G. Szymanski. Lower bounds and reductions between grammar problems. *J. Assoc. Comput. Mach.* 25 (1978), 32-51.

153. H.B. Hunt III. A complexity theory of grammar problems. Conf. Record of the Third ACM Symp. on *Principles of Programming Languages,* 1976, 12-18.

154. H.B. Hunt III and D.J. Rosenkrantz. Complexity of grammatical similarity relations. Proc. of a Conf. on *Theoretical Computer Science,* Waterloo, Ontario, 1977, 139-145.

155. H.B. Hunt III, T.G. Szymanski and J.D. Ullman. Operations on sparse relations, with applications to grammar problems. Proc. of the Fifteenth Annual Symp. on *Switching and Automata Theory,* 1974, 127-132.

156. H.B. Hunt and T.G. Szymanski. Corregendum to lower bounds and reduction between grammar problems. *J. Assoc. Comput. Mach.* 25 (1978), 687-688.

157. H.B. Hunt III. Observations on the complexity of regular expression problems. *J. Comput. System Sci.* 19 (1979), 222-236.

158. H. Hunt and D.J. Rosenkrantz. Efficient algorithms for structural similarity of grammars. Conf. record of Seventh ACM Symp. on *Principles of Programming Languages,* 1980, 213-219.

159. H.B. Hunt III. On the decidability of grammar problems. Technical Report 80-9, Dept. of Computer Science, State University of New York at Albany, 1980.

160. H.B. Hunt III. On the decidability of grammar problems. *J. Assoc. Comput. Mach.* 29 (1982), 429-447.

161. R.B. Hunter, A.D. McGettrick and R. Patel. LL versus LR parsing with illustrations from Algol 68. *SIGPLAN Notices* 12, Nr.6, June 1977, 49-53.

162. R. Hunter. *The Design and Construction of Compilers.* John Wiley and Sons, New York, 1981.

163. E.T. Irons. A syntax-directed compiler for ALGOL 60. *Comm. ACM* 4 (1961), 51-55.

164. E.T. Irons. An error-correcting parse algorithm. *Comm. ACM* 6 (1963), 669-673.

165. B. Jankov. A method for translating and implementing programming languages. *Programmirovanie* 1980, No.1, 41-50, 95 (Russian); translated as *Program. Comput. Software* 6 (1980), No.1, 31-39.

166. S. Jarzabek and T. Krawczyk. LL-regular grammars. *Prace Instytutu Maszyn Matemaycznych* 16 (1974), 95-106 and *Prace IMM* 17 (1975), 107-116.

167. S. Jarzabek and T. Krawczyk. LL-regular grammars. *Information Processing Letters* 4 (1975), 31-37.

168. D.B. Johnson and R. Sethi. Efficient construction of LL(1) parsers. Techn. Report 164, Computer Science Department, Pennsylvania State University, March 1975.

169. D.B. Johnson and R. Sethi. A characterization of LL(1) grammars. *BIT (Nordisk Tidskrift for Informationsbehandling)* 16 (1976), 275-280.

170. K. Kaijiri. On an error recovery scheme for recursive descent parsers. *Trans. Inst. Electron. & Comm. Eng. Jpn.* (Japan), Vol.E64, No.10, 690-690, 1981.

171. E. Kalisz. LL(1) grammars and predictive deterministic parsing (in Rumanian). *Bul. Inst. Politeh. Gheorghe Gheorghiu-Dej*, Bucuresti Ser. Electroteh, Vol.40, No.4, Oct.-Dec. 1978, 93-100.

172. F.P. Kaminger. Syntax definition by means of recursive graphs. IBM Laboratory Vienna, Techn. Report TR 25.078, 1968.

173. F.P. Kaminger. Generation, recognition and parsing of context-free languages by means of recursive graphs. *Computing* 11 (1973), 87-96.

174. G.A.M. Kamsteeg-Kemper. Analyse methode bottom-to-top en top-to-bottom gekombineerd (in Dutch). ALG. VGP 062, Manuscript, Vakgroep Informatica, Twente University of Technology, 1972.

175. H. Kanner, P. Kosinski and C.L. Robinson. The structure of yet another ALGOL compiler. *Comm. ACM* 8 (1965), 427-438.

176. R.J.W. Kershaw. An error-tolerant top-down parser. Royal Radar Establishment, Malvern, England, May 1974, AD/A-002 889/4WC.

177. K.N. King. Intercalation theorems for families of strict deterministic languages. Technical Report UCB-CS-KK-78-01, University of California, Berkeley, California, 1978.

178. K.N. King. Intercalation theorems for families of strict deterministic languages. *Theoret. Comput. Sci.* 10 (1980), 317-333.

179. A. Kley and B. Johnson. Was ist rekursiver Abstieg? *Elektronische Rechenanlagen* 17 (1975), 180-188.

180. D.E. Knuth. A history of writing compilers. *Computers and Automation* 11 (1962), 8-14.

181. D.E. Knuth. Top-down syntax analysis. Lect. Notes Int. Summer School on Computer Programming, Copenhagen, 1967. Also: *Acta Informatica* 1 (1971), 79-110.

182. T. Komor. On a property of modified factored grammars. *USSR Comput. Math. and Math. Phys.* 12 (1972), 319-325.

183. T. Komor. Transforming grammars into factored form. Ph.D. Thesis, University of Moscow, 1973.

184. T. Komor. Transforming grammars into factored form. Proc. of the *Computer Science Conference*, Szekesfehervan, Hungary, 1973.

185. T. Komor. A note on left factored languages. *Computer Journal* 17 (1974), 242-244.

186. T. Kopriva. A contribution to the top-to-bottom recognizer rehabilitation. *Kybernetika* 3 (1968), 193-200.

187. A.J. Korenjak and J.E. Hopcroft. Simple deterministic grammars. Conf. Record of Seventh Annual Symp. on *Switching and Automata Theory*, 1966, 36-46.

188. C.H.A. Koster. Using the CDL compiler-compiler. In: *Compiler Construction: An Advanced Course.* F.L. Bauer and J. Eickel (eds.), Lect. Notes in Comp. Sci. 21, Springer-Verlag, Berlin, 1974, 366-426.

189. C.H.A. Koster. A technique for parsing ambiguous languages. *GI-4.Jahrestagung,* D. Siefkes (ed.), Lect. Notes in Comp. Sci. 26, Springer-Verlag, Berlin, 1975, 234-246.

190. J. Kral and J. Demner. A note on the number of states of the DeRemer's recognizer. *Information Processing Letters* 2 (1973), 22-23.

191. J. Kral. Semi-top-down transition diagrams driven syntactic analysis. Part II. In: Report UVT 6/73/M, Technical University of Prague, 1973.

192. J. Kral. Bottom-up versus top-down syntax analysis revised. Report UVT 10/74, Technical University of Prague, 1974.

193. J. Kral. Top-down versus bottom-up syntax analysis revised. In: *Mathematical Foundations of Computer Science*, A. Blikle (ed.), Lect. Notes in Comp. Sci. 28, Springer-Verlag, Berlin, 1974, 256-273.

194. J. Kral. The top-down analysis from the point of view of a compiler writer. *Acta Polytechnica* 4 (1974).

195. J. Kral. Semi-top-down transition diagrams driven syntax analysis. Report UVT 11/74, Technical University of Prague, 1974.

196. J. Kral and J. Demner. Parsing as a subtask of compiling. In: *Mathematical Foundations of Computer Science*, J. Becvar (ed.), Lect. Notes in Comp. Sci. 32, Springer-Verlag, Berlin, 1975, 61-74.

197. J. Kral. Almost top-down analysis for generalized LR(k) grammars. In: *Methods of Algorithmic Language Implementation*, A. Ershov and C.H.A. Koster (eds.), Lect. Notes in Comp. Sci. 47, Springer-Verlag, Berlin, 1977, 149-172.

198. J. Kral. A top-down no backtracking parsing of general context-free languages. In: *Mathematical Foundations of Computer Science*, J. Gruska (ed.), Lect. Notes in Comp. Sci. 53, Springer-Verlag, Berlin, 1977, 333-341.

199. B. Kraemer and H.W. Schmidt. Locally nondeterministic and hybrid syntax analyzers from partitioned two-level grammars. In: *GI-9.Jahrestagung*, K.H. Boehling and P.P. Spies (eds.), Informatik Fachberichte 19, Springer-Verlag, Berlin, 1979 194-205.

200. M. Kretinsky. Semi-top-down syntax analysis of precedence grammars. *Scripta Fac. Sci. Natur. UJEP Brunensis Math.* 8 (1978), 1-11.

201. S. Kuno and A.G. Oettinger. Multiple-path syntactic analyzer. *Information Processing 62*. C.M. Popplewell (ed.), North-Holland Publ. Co., Amsterdam, 1963, 306-311.

202. S. Kuno. The augmented predictive analyzer for context-free languages - its relative efficiency. *Comm. ACM* 9 (1966), 810-823.

203. S. Kuno. The predictive analyzer and a path elimination technique. *Comm. ACM* 8 (1965), 453-462.

204. R. Kurki-Suonio. A note on LL(1) languages. Int. Summer School on Computer Programming, Copenhagen, 1967.

205. R. Kurki-Suonio. On top-to-bottom recognition and left recursion. *Comm. ACM* 9 (1966), 527-528.

206. R. Kurki-Suonio. Notes on top-down languages. *BIT (Nordisk Tidskrift for Informationsbehandling)* 9 (1969), 225-238.

207. V.F. Kuzenko. Push-down transducers and the syntactic analysis of certain classes of grammars (Russian). *Akad. Nauk Ukrain. SSR,* Ser. A, 1976, No.1, 73-75, 96. [MR 54#6570, 1977].

208. V.F. Kuzenko. Two classes of context-free grammars with a decidable equivalence problem (Russian). *Akad. Nauk Ukrain. SSR,* Inst. Kibernet., Preprint No.3 (1978), 16-23.

209. V.F. Kuzenko. Equivalent transformations of definitions of programming languages. *Program. Comput. Software* 5 (1979), 86-92.

210. H.W. Lawson and D.R. Doucette. A translation machine with automated top-down parsing. *SIGPLAN Notices* 11, Nr.2, February 1976, 20-29.

211. J. van Leeuwen. An elementary proof that a certain context-free language is not LL(k) and a generalization. Notes, 6 October 1972.

212. B.L. Leong and D. Wotschke. The influence of productions on derivations and parsing. Conf. record of the Third ACM Symp. on *Principles of Programming Languages,* 1976, 1-11.

213. J.W. Lewi, K. de Vlaminck, J. Huens and M. Huybrechts. Project LILA, the ELL(1) generator, basic principles. Report CWS, Kath. Universiteit Leuven, 1976.

214. J.W. Lewi, K. de Vlaminck, J. Huens and M. Huybrechts. Project LILA: The ELL(1) generator of LILA, an introduction. *Intern. Computing Symposium 1977,* Proc., E. Morlet and D. Ribbons (eds.), North-Holland Publ. Co., Amsterdam, 1977, 237-251.

215. J.W. Lewi, K. de Vlaminck, J. Huens and M. Huybrechts. The ELL(1) parser generator and the error-recovery mechanism. *Acta Informatica* 10 (1978), 209-228.

216. J.W. Lewi, K. de Vlaminck, J. Huens and M. Huybrechts. *Methodology in Compiler Construction.* Part I: Concepts, 1979. Part II: Implementation, 1982. North-Holland Publ. Co., Amsterdam.

217. P.M. Lewis II and R.E. Stearns. Syntax-directed transduction. IEEE Seventh Annual Symp. on *Switching and Automata Theory*, 1966, 21-35.

218. P.M. Lewis II and R.E. Stearns. Syntax-directed transduction. *J. Assoc. Comput. Mach.* 15 (1968), 464-488.

219. P.M. Lewis II and D.J. Rosenkrantz. An ALGOL compiler designed using automata theory. Proc. Symp. on *Computers and Automata,* Microwave Research Institute Symposia Series, 21 (1971), 75-88. Polytechnic Institute of Brooklyn, N.Y.

220. P.M. Lewis, D.J. Rosenkrantz and R.E. Stearns. Attributed translations. *J. Comput. System Sci.* 9 (1974), 297-307.

221. P.M. Lewis II, D.J. Rosenkrantz and R.E. Stearns. *Compiler Design Theory.* Addison-Wesley, Reading, Mass., 1976.

222. G. Lindstrom. Control structure aptness: a case study using top-down parsing. In: Proc. 3rd Int. Conf. on *Software Engineering*, 1978, 5-12.

223. J.J. Linn. Augmented predictive parsing grammars. *ACM Comp. Sci. Conf.,* Dayton, Ohio, 1979.

224. D.B. Lomet. The construction of efficient deterministic language processors. Ph.D. Thesis, Univ. of Pennsylvania, Philadelphia, 1969.

225. D.B. Lomet. A formalization of transition diagram systems. *J. Assoc. Comput. Mach.* 20 (1973), 235-257.

226. D.B. Lomet. Automatic generation of multiple exit parsing subroutines. In: *Automata, Languages and Programming,* J. Loeckx (ed.), Lect. Notes in Comp. Sci. 14, Springer-Verlag, Berlin, 1974, 214-231.

227. P. Lucas. Die Strukturanalyse von Formeluebersetzern. *Elektronische Rechenanlagen* 3 (1961), 159-167.

228. M. Madsen and N.D. Jones. Letting the attributes influence the parsing. Manuscript, undated.

229. M. Madsen. Parsing attribute grammars. Doctoral Thesis, Dept. of Computer Science, University of Aarhus, Denmark, February 1980.

230. J. Mauney and C.N. Fischer. An improvement to immediate error detection in strong LL(1) parsers. *Information Processing Letters* 12 (1981), 211-212.

231. J. Mauney and C.N. Fischer. A forward move algorithm for LL and LR parsers. ACM SIGPLAN Symp. on *Compiler Construction*, 1982.

232. O. Mayer. *Syntaxanalyse*. Bibliographisches Institut Mannheim, 1978.

233. W.M. McKeeman. Compiler construction. In: *Compiler Construction: An Advanced Course*. F.L. Bauer and J. Eickel (eds.), Lect. Notes in Comp. Sci. 21, Springer-Verlag, Berlin, 1974, 1-36.

234. L. Meertens and H. van Vliet. Parsing ALGOL68 with syntax-directed error recovery. In: *ALGOL 68*. Proc. of the 1975 Int. Conf. on ALGOL68. G.E. Hedrick (ed.), Oklahoma State University, Stillwater, 1975, 118-155.

235. K. Mehlhorn. Parsing macro grammars top-down. *Information and Control* 40 (1979), 123-143.

236. R.W. Meijer. A note on "LL versus LR parsing with illustrations from ALGOL 68". *SIGPLAN Notices* 12, Nr.12, December 1977, 30-32.

237. H. Meijer and A. Nijholt. Translator writing tools since 1970: A selective bibliography. *SIGPLAN Notices*, 1982, to appear.

238. H.H. Metcalfe. A parameterized compiler based on mechanical linguistics. *Ann. Reviews Aut. Programming* 4 (1964), Pergamon Press, 125-165.

239. D.R. Milton. Syntactic specification and analysis using attribute grammars. Ph.D. Thesis, Computer Sciences Dept., Tech. Report #304, University of Wisconsin-Madison, 1977.

240. D.R. Milton, L.W. Kirchhoff and B.R. Rowland. An ALL(1) compiler generator. Proc. of the SIGPLAN Symp. on *Compiler Construction*. *SIGPLAN Notices* 14, Nr.8, August 1979, 152-157.

241. D.R. Milton and C.N. Fischer. LL(k) parsing for attributed grammars. In: *Automata, Languages and Programming*, H.A. Maurer (ed.), Lect. Notes in Comp. Sci. 71, Springer-Verlag, Berlin, 1979, 422-430.

242. A.V. Moura. Syntactic equivalence of grammar classes. Ph.D. Thesis, University of California, Berkeley, September 1980.

243. A. Sh. Nepomnyaschaya. A generalization of LL(k) grammars that is oriented toward effective syntactic analysis (Russian). *Programmirovanie* 1976, No.3, 13-21, 87. [MR 55#1848, 1978].

244. A. Sh. Nepomnyaschaya. Generalization of LL(k) grammars containing non-single-valued grammars, and the problem of syntactic analysis. *Program. Comput. Software* 5 (1979), 309-317.

245. A. Nijholt. On the parsing of LL-regular grammars. In: *Mathematical Foundations of Computer Science,* A. Mazurkiewicz (ed.), Lect. Notes in Comp. Sci. 45, Springer-Verlag, Berlin, 1976, 446-452.

246. A. Nijholt. On the covering of left recursive grammars. Conf. Record of the Fourth ACM Symp. on *Principles of Programming Languages,* 1977, 86-96.

247. A. Nijholt. On the covering of parsable grammars. *J. Comput. System Sci.* 15 (1977), 99-110.

248. A. Nijholt. Simple chain grammars. In: *Automata, Languages and Programming,* A. Salomaa and M. Steinby (eds.), Lect. Notes in Comp. Sci. 52, Springer-Verlag, Berlin, 1977, 352-364.

249. A. Nijholt. On the parsing and covering of simple chain grammars. In: *Automata, Languages and Programming,* G. Ausiello and C. Bohm (eds.), Lect. Notes in Comp. Sci. 62, Springer-Verlag, Berlin, 1978, 330-344.

250. A. Nijholt. A left part theorem for grammatical trees. *Discrete Mathematics* 25 (1979), 51-63.

251. A. Nijholt. Simple chain grammars and languages. *Theoret. Comp. Sci.* 9 (1979), 287-309.

252. A. Nijholt. Structure preserving transformations of non-left-recursive grammars. In: *Automata, Languages and Programming,* H.A. Maurer (ed.), Lect. Notes in Comp. Sci. 71, Springer-Verlag, Berlin, 1979, 446-459.

253. A. Nijholt and E. Soisalon-Soininen. Ch(k) grammars: A characterization of LL(k) languages. In: *Mathematical Foundations of Computer Science,* J. Becvar (ed.), Lect. Notes in Comp. Sci. 74, Springer-Verlag, Berlin, 1979, 390-397.

254. A. Nijholt. Grammar functors and covers: From non-left-recursive to Greibach normal form grammars. *BIT (Nordisk Tidskrift for Informationsbehandling)* 19 (1979), 73-78.

255. A. Nijholt. *Context-Free Grammars: Covers, Normal Forms, and Parsing.* Lect. Notes in Comp. Sci. 93, Springer-Verlag, Berlin, 1980.

256. A. Nijholt. LL-regular grammars. *Int. J. Computer Math.* 8 (1980), 303-318.

257. A. Nijholt. A framework for classes of grammars between the LL(k) and LR(k) grammars. CSTR No. 80-CS-25, McMaster University, Hamilton, Ontario, 1980.

258. A. Nijholt. Parsing strategies: A concise survey. In: *Mathematical Foundations of Computer Science,* J. Gruska and M. Chytil (eds.), Lect. Notes in Comp. Sci. 118, Springer-Verlag, Berlin, 1981, 103-120.

259. A. Nijholt. The equivalence problem for LL- and LR- regular grammars. In: *Fundamentals of Computation Theory,* F. Gecseg (ed.), Lect. Notes in Comp. Sci. 117, Springer-Verlag, Berlin, 1981, 291-300.

260. A. Nijholt. The equivalence problem for LL- and LR- regular grammars. *J. Comput. System Sci.* 24 (1982), 149-161.

261. A. Nijholt. From LL-regular to LL(1) grammars: transformations, covers, and parsing. *RAIRO Informatique Theorique,* to appear.

262. A. Nijholt. On satisfying the LL-iteration theorem. In: Report IR-33, June 1982, Katholieke Universiteit Nijmegen. Also: *Theoret. Comput. Sci.,* to appear.

263. A. Nijholt. On the relationship between the LL(k) and LR(k) grammars. Report IR-34, Katholieke Universiteit Nijmegen, June 1982. To appear in *Information Processing Letters.*

264. A. Nijholt. Precedence relations: A bibliography. *SIGACT News,* Vol.14, Nr.2, Spring 1982, 9-19.

265. A. Nijholt and J. Pittl. A general scheme for some deterministically parsable grammars and their strong equivalents. Report IR-38, Katholieke Universiteit Nijmegen, August 1982. To appear in Proc. of the 6th G.I. Conference on *Theoretical Informatics,* Dortmund, 1983.

266. N.S. Nikitchenko and S.S. Skil'njak. Syntactic analysis of programming languages by the "top-down" method (in Russian). *Programmirovanie* 1975, No.6, Nov.-Dec., 3-11.

267. N.S. Nikitcenko. The equivalence problem in the class of GL(k) grammars (Russian). *Akad. Nauk Ukrain. SSR,* Inst. Kibernet., Preprint No.3 (1978), 24-32.

268. O. Nurmi, M. Sarjakoski and S. Sippu. The HLP'84 project. Manuscript, Dept. of Computer Science, University of Helsinki, March 1982.

269. O. Nurmi, M. Sarjakoski and S. Sippu. HLP 84 -   A tool for compiler writing. Manuscript, Dept. of Computer Science, University of Helsinki, May 1982.

270. T. Olshansky and A. Pnueli. A direct algorithm for checking equivalence of LL(k) grammars. *Theoret. Comput. Sci.* 4 (1977), 321-349.

271. T.J. Ostrand, M.C. Paull and E.J. Weynker. Parsing regular grammars with finite look-ahead. *Acta Informatica* 16 (1981), 125-138.

272. A.G. Oettinger. Automatic syntactic analysis and the pushdown store. In: *Structure of Language and its Mathematical Aspects.* Proc. of Symposia in Appl. Math., Vol.XII, R. Jakobson (ed.), American Mathematical Society, Providence, Rhode Island, 1961, 104-129.

273. A.B. Pai. Syntax driven error recovery in top-down parsing. Ph.D. Thesis, Dept. of Computer Science, SUNY at Stony Brook, August 1978.

274. A.B. Pai and R.B. Kieburtz. Global context recovery: a new strategy for parser recovery from syntax errors. Proc. of the SIGPLAN Symp. on *Compiler Construction. SIGPLAN Notices* 14, Nr.8, August 1979, 158-167.

275. A.B. Pai and R.B. Kieburtz. Global context recovery: a new strategy for parser recovery from syntax errors. *ACM Trans. Progr. Lang. Syst.* 2 (1980), 18-41.

276. C. Pair. Toute grammaire LL(k) est LR(k) (suite). *RAIRO Informatique Theorique* 9 (1974), 59-62.

277. R. Parchmann, J. Duske and J. Specht. Indexed LL(k) grammars. I. Basic concepts and strong indexed LL(k) grammars. Manuscript, Institut fuer Informatik, Universitaet Hannover, 1982.

278. R. Parchmann, J. Duske and J. Specht. Indexed LL(k) grammars. II. The decidability of the indexed LL(k) property. Manuscript, Institut fuer Informatik, Universitaet Hannover, 1982.

279. M.C. Paull and S.H. Unger. Structural equivalence of context-free grammars. *J. Comput. System Sci.* 2 (1968), 427-463.

280. M.C. Paull and S.H. Unger. Structural equivalence of LL(k) grammars. IEEE Conf. Record of 9th Annual Symp. on *Switching and Automata Theory*, 1968, 176-186.

281. R.H. Pierce and J. Rowell. A transformation-directed compiling system. *Computer Journal* 20 (1977), 109-115.

282. J. Pittl. On LLP(k) grammars and languages. *Theoret. Comput. Sci.* 16 (1981), 149-175.

283. J. Pittl. On LLP(k) parsers. *J. Comput. System Sci.* 24 (1982), 36-68.

284. U.F. Pleban. The use of transition matrices in a recursive descent compiler. Proc. of the SIGPLAN Symp. on *Compiler Construction. SIGPLAN Notices* 14, Nr.8, August 1979, 144-151.

285. B.W. Pollack (ed.). *Compiler Techniques.* Auerbach Publishers, Philadelphia, 1972.

286. D.A. Poplawski. Properties of LL-regular languages. CSD-TR-241, Purdue University, 1977.

287. D.A. Poplawski. Error recovery for extended LL-regular parsers. Purdue University, Ph.D. Thesis, August 1978.

288. D.A. Poplawski. On LL-regular grammars. *J. Comput. System Sci.* 18 (1979), 218-227.

289. D. Potocan. Die Simulation der prozedurorientierten Syntaxanalyse mit Fehlerbehandlung auf deterministischen Kellerautomaten. Dissertation, Phil. Fak. der Universitaet Innsbruck, 1975.

290. R.E. Prather. Minimal solutions of Paull-Unger problems. *Math. Systems Theory* 3 (1969), 76-85.

291. V.R. Pratt. Top-down operator precedence. Proc. of the ACM Symp. on *Principles of Programming Languages*, Boston, 1973, 41-51.

292. A. Pyster. *Compiler Design and Construction.* Van Nostrand Reinhold, 1980.

293. A. Pyster. ZUSE User's manual. TRCS 81-04, Dept. of Computer Science, University of California, Santa Barbara, 1981.

294. A. Pyster. ZUSE: An LL(1) based translator writing system for Unix. *SIGPLAN Notices* 16, Nr.3, March 1981, p.6.

295. K.-J. Raiha and M. Saarinen. Developments in compiler writing systems. In: *GI-6.Jahrestagung,* E.J. Neuhold (ed.), Informatik Fachberichte 5, Springer-Verlag, Berlin, 1976, 164-178.

296. K.-J. Raiha and E. Ukkonen. Balancing syntactic and semantic power in compiler construction. *Information Processing 80.* S.H. Lavington (ed.), North-Holland Publ. Co., Amsterdam, 1980, 65-70.

297. P. Rechenberg. Sackgassenfreie Syntaxanalyse. *Elek- tronische Rechenanlagen* 15 (1973), 119-125 and 170-176.

298. P. Rechenberg. Fehlererkennung bei der Pseudo-LL(1)-Analyse. ACM/German Chapter Lectures I/II, 1973.

299. J. Reichardt. Analysierbarkeit und Normalformentransformation kontextfreier Grammatiken. TI-1/79, Universitaet Darmstadt, 1979.

300. J.C. Reynolds. An introduction to the COGENT programming system. Proc. 20th *National ACM Conf.,* Vol.20, August 1965, 422-436.

301. J. Roehrich. Automatic construction of error correcting parsers. Ph.D. Thesis, Int. Bericht Nr.8, Fakultaet fuer Informatik, Universitaet Karlsruhe, 1978.

302. J. Roehrich. Methods for the automatic construction of error correcting parsers. *Acta Informatica* 13 (1980), 115-139.

303. S. Rosen. A compiler-building system developed by Brooker and Morris. *Comm. ACM* 7 (1964), 403-414.

304. S. Rosen (ed.). *Programming Systems and Languages.* McGraw-Hill, New York, 1967.

305. D.J. Rosenkrantz. Matrix equations and normal forms for context-free grammars. *J. Assoc. Comput. Mach.* 14 (1967), 501-507.

306. D.J. Rosenkrantz and R.E. Stearns. Properties of deterministic top-down grammars. Proc. ACM Symp. on the *Theory of Computing,* 1969, 181-190.

307. D.J. Rosenkrantz and P.M. Lewis II. Deterministic left corner parsing. Proc. 11th Annual IEEE Symp. on *Switching and Automata Theory,* 1970, 139-152.

308. D.J. Rosenkrantz and R.E. Stearns. Properties of deterministic top-down grammars. *Information and Control* 17 (1970), 226-256.

309. R.J. Ross. Grammar transformations based on regular decompositions of context-free derivations. Ph.D. Thesis, Washington State University, Pullman, Dept. of Computer Science, 1978.

310. R.J. Ross, G. Hotz and D.B. Benson. A general Greibach normal form transformation. Report CS-78-048, Dept. of Computer Science, Washington State University, Pullman, Washington, 1978.

311. B.R. Rowland. Combining parsing and evaluation for attributed grammars. Ph.D. Thesis, University of Wisconsin-Madison, 1977.

312. P. Ruzicka. On the size of DeRemer's analyzer. *Kybernetika* (Prague) 11 (1975), 207-217.

313. H. Samet. A coroutine approach to parsing. *ACM Trans. Progr. Lang. Syst.* 2 (1980), 290-306.

314. P. Schlichtiger. Kettengrammatiken: Ein Konzept zur Definition handhabbarer Grammatikklassen mit effizientem Analyseverhalten. Ph.D. Thesis, Universitaet Kaiserslautern, 1979.

315. P. Schlichtiger. Partitioned chain grammars. In: *Automata, Languages and Programming*, J.W. de Bakker and J. van Leeuwen (eds.), Lect. Notes in Comp. Sci. 85, Springer-Verlag, Berlin, 1980, 555-568.

316. D.V. Schorre. META II, a syntax oriented compiler writing language. Proc. *ACM Nat. Conf.* 19, D1.3.1-D1.3.11, 1964.

317. D. V. Schorre. A necessary and sufficient condition for a context-free language to be unambiguous. SDC Document SP-2153.

318. R.W. Sebesta. Parsable subclasses of extensions to context-free grammars. Ph.D. Thesis, Pennsylvania State University, PA, 1974.

319. R.W. Sebesta. Top-down nondirectional parser. *ACM Comp. Sci. Conf.*, Washington, DC, 1975, p.40.

320. R.W. Sebesta and N.D. Jones. Parsers for indexed grammars. *Int. J. Comput. Inform. Sci.* 7 (1978), 345-359.

321. H. Seeger. Fehlerbehandlung in LL-Parsern. Diplomarbeit, Technische Universitaet Muenchen, Institut fuer Informatik, 1977.

322. S. Sekimoto. A characterization of look-ahead stateless DPDA's of a bottom-up type. *Trans. Inst. Electron. & Comm. Eng. Jpn.* (Japan), Vol.E63, No.6, 490-491, 1980.

323. V.W. Setzer. Non recursive top-down syntax analysis. *Software - Practice and Experience* 9 (1979), 237-245.

324. V.V. Sevcenko. The parametrization of LL(k) grammars. *Software of Electronic Digital Computers.* Proceedings, 1971. Akad. Nauk Ukrain. SSR, Inst. Kibernet., Kiev, 69-85.

325. V.V. Sevcenko. On the question of deterministic methods for top-down analysis. *Software of Electronic Digital Computers.* Proceedings, 1971. Akad. Nauk Ukrain. SSR, Inst. Kibernet., Kiev, 86-98.

326. V.V. Sevcenko. A certain approach to the problem of syntactical analysis (Russian). *Kibernetika* (Kiev) 1974, No.4, 30-38. [MR 53#12112, 1977].

327. B.A. Sheil. Observations on context-free parsing. Harvard University, Center for Research in Computing Technology, TR-12-76, 1976. Also: *SMIL* (Stockholm), 1976.

328. R.K. Shyamasundar. An efficient LL(1) parser generating system. *J. Comput. Soc. India* 8 (1977), 17-21.

329. B.A. Silverberg. Using a grammatical formalism as a programming language. Tech. Report CSRG-88, January 1978, University of Toronto.

330. B.P. Sindeev. Transformation algorithm to produce syntax in a form convenient for single-pass compiling. *Programmirovanie* 1975, No.4, July-Aug., 36-44.

331. S. Sippu and E. Soisalon-Soininen. On constructing LL(k) parsers. In: *Automata, Languages and Programming,* H.A. Maurer (ed.), Lect. Notes in Comp. Sci. 71, Springer-Verlag, Berlin, 1979, 585-595.

332. S. Sippu and E. Soisalon-Soininen. Characterizations of the LL(k) property. In: *Automata, Languages and Programming,* J.W. de Bakker and J. van Leeuwen (eds.), Lect. Notes in Comp. Sci. 85, Springer-Verlag, Berlin, 1980, 596-608.

333. S. Sippu and E. Soisalon-Soininen. Compact LL(1) parsing with immediate error detection. Manuscript, Dept. of Computer Science, University of Helsinki, in preparation.

334. S.S. Skil'njak. Classification of syntactical definitions that are oriented towards the strategy of scanning (Russian). In: *Questions in the Constr. of Progr. Systems* (Russian) 89-103. Inst. Kibernet., Akad. Nauk Ukrain. SSR, Kiev, 1978.

335. I. Sklenar. Corrections of lexical errors in ALGOL 68 programs. Proc. of the 5th Annual III Conf. *Implementation and Design of Algorithmic Languages.* J. Andre and J.-P. Banatre (eds.), 1977, 183-189.

336. E. Soisalon-Soininen and E. Ukkonen. A characterization of LL(k) languages. In: *Automata, Languages and Programming,* S. Michaelson and R. Milner (eds.), Third Coll., Edinburgh University Press, Edinburgh, 1976, 20-30.

337. E. Soisalon-Soininen. Characterization of LL(k) languages by restricted LR(k) grammars. Ph.D. Thesis, University of Helsinki, 1977.

338. E. Soisalon-Soininen and E. Ukkonen. A method for transforming grammars into LL(k) form. *Acta Informatica* 12 (1979), 339-369.

339. E. Soisalon-Soininen. On the covering problem for left-recursive grammars. *Theoret. Comput. Sci.* 8 (1979), 1-11.

340. E. Soisalon-Soininen. On comparing LL(k) and LR(k) grammars. *Math. Systems Theory* 13 (1980), 323-329.

341. R.E. Stearns. Deterministic top-down parsing. Proc. of Fifth Annual Princeton Conf. on *Information Sciences and Systems,* 1971, 182-189.

342. H.S. Stone. One pass compilation of arithmetic expressions for a parallel preprocessor. *Comm. ACM* 10 (1967), 220-223.

343. W.R. Strait. Formal model of translation with symbol table pointers. *ACM Comp. Sci. Conf.,* Washington, DC, 1975, p.40.

344. I. Streinu. LL(k) languages are closed under union with finite languages. In: *Automata, Languages and Programming,* A. Salomaa and M. Steinby (eds.), Lect. Notes in Comp. Sci. 52, Springer-Verlag, Berlin, 1977, 504-508.

345. I. Streinu. The Darboux property for the hierarchy of LL(k) languages (Romanian, English summary). *Stud. Cerc. Mat* 30 (1978), 579-593.

346. R. Strobel. Top-down analysis of context-free grammars with ambiguous parentheses. *Elektronische Informationsverarbeitung und Kybernetik (EIK)* 11 (1975), 381-385.

347. R. Strobel. Some automatic transformations of CF-grammars. In: *Methods of Algorithmic Language Implementation*, A. Ershov and C.H.A. Koster (eds.), Lect. Notes in Comp. Sci. 47, Springer-Verlag, Berlin, 1977, 218-230.

348. W. Struckmann, U. Horstmann and A. Uhde. Ein Syntax-analyseverfahren fuer geklammerte zweischichtige Grammatiken. In: *Compiler-Compiler*. W. Henhapl (ed.), 3. GI-Fachgespraech, Muenchen, March 1982, 75-88.

349. P. Szabo. Der allgemeine LL-Akzeptor. Int. Bericht 1978/3, Institut fuer Informatik, Universitaet Karlsruhe.

350. T.G. Szymanski and J.D. Ullman. Evaluating relational expressions with dense and sparse arguments. *SIAM J. Computing* 6 (1977), 109-122.

351. G. Terrine. An algorithm generating the decision table of deterministic bottom-up parser for a subset of context-free grammars. Proc. of the Third Annual ACM Symp. on *Theory of Computing*, 1971, 185-205.

352. G. Terrine and A.M. Couhault. LL(k) parsing by canonical pda using bounded context technique. IRIA Lab. Research Report No. 222, 1977.

353. G. Terrine. Coordinate grammars and parsers. *Computer Journal* 16 (1973), 232-244.

354. D. Thimm. Kombination von sackgassenfreier Topdown- und Bottomup-Syntaxanalyse. *GI-5.Jahrestagung*, J. Muehlbacher (ed.), Lect. Notes in Comp. Sci. 34, Springer-Verlag, Berlin, 1975, 397-408.

355. D. Thimm. Effiziente Algorithmen zur Syntaxanalyse von Programmiersprachen. Dissertation, Technische Universitaet Berlin, Institut fuer Technische Informatik, 1977.

356. D. Thimm. Kombinierte Topdown/Bottomup-Syntaxanalyse von LR(k)-Grammatiken. *Elektronische Rechenanlagen* 20 (1978), 5.

357. R.A. Thompson and T.L. Booth. Encoding of probabilistic context-free languages. In: *Theory of Machines and Computations*. Z. Kohavi and A. Paz (eds.), Academic Press, New York, 1971, 169-186.

358. V. Tixier. Recursive functions of regular expressions in language analysis. Doctoral dissertation, Computer Science Department, Stanford University, CS 58, 1967.

359. T. Tokuda and K. Inoue. New LL(k) parsers and the computational complexity of their minimization problems (in Japanese). *Inf. Process. Soc. Jpn.* 19 (1978), No.5, 436-443.

360. E. Tomita. A more direct algorithm for checking equivalence of LL(k) grammars. *Trans. Inst. Electron. & Comm. Eng. Jpn.* (Japan), Vol.E63, No.9, 690-690, 1980.

361. E. Tomita. A direct branching algorithm for checking equivalence of strict deterministic vs. LL(k) grammars. *Theoret. Comput. Sci.*, to appear.

362. E. Tomcha, K. Sakuramoto and T. Kasai. A top-down parsing algorithm for a context-sensitive language. *Trans. Inst. Electron. & Comm. Eng. Jpn.* (Japan), Vol.E62, No.2, 127-128, Febr. 1979.

363. R.W. Topor. A note on error recovery in recursive descent parsers. *SIGPLAN Notices* 17, Nr.2, February 1982, 37-40.

364. G.E. Tseytlin and E.L. Yushchenko. Several aspects of theory of parametric models of languages and parallel syntactic analysis. In: *Methods of Algorithmic Language Implementation*. A. Ershov and C.H.A. Koster (eds.), Lect. Notes in Comp. Sci. 47, Springer-Verlag, Berlin, 1977, 231-245.

365. D.A. Turner. Error diagnosis and recovery in one pass compilers. *Information Processing Letters* 8 (1977), 113-115.

366. E. Ukkonen. A modification of the LR(k) method for constructing compact bottom-up parsers. In: *Automata, Languages and Programming,* H.A. Maurer (ed.), Lect. Notes in Comp. Sci. 71, Springer-Verlag, Berlin, 1979, 646-658.

367. E. Ukkonen. On size bounds for deterministic parsers. In: *Automata, Languages and Programming,* S. Even and O. Kariv (eds.), Lect. Notes in Comp. Sci. 115, Springer-Verlag, Berlin, 1981, 218-228.

368. E. Ukkonen. Lower bounds on the size of deterministic parsers. Mem. No. UCB/ERL M81/98, October 1981, University of California, Berkeley.

369. J.D. Ullman. Applications of language theory to compiler design. In: *Currents in the Theory of Computing,* A.V. Aho (ed.), Prentice Hall, Englewood Cliffs, N.J., 1973, 173-218.

370. S.M. Unger. A global parser for context-free phrase structure grammars. *Comm. ACM* 11 (1968), 240-247.

371. L.G. Valiant. Regularity and related problems for deterministic pushdown automata. *J. Assoc. Comput. Mach.* 22 (1975), 1-10.

372. D. Varga. Problems of improving the efficiencies of parsing systems. *Computational Linguistics* 8 (1970), 71-93.

373. J. Vidart. Extensions syntaxiques dans une contexte LL(1). These 3.cycle, Universite de Grenoble, France, 1974.

374. J.C. van Vliet. The programs "Relations concerning a CF-grammar" and "LL(1)-checker". Report IN 4/73, Mathematisch Centrum, Amsterdam, 1973.

375. Vu-Luc. On necessary and sufficient conditions of the LF grammars (in Hungarian). *Alkalmazott Mat. Lapok* (Hungarian), Vol.2, No.3-4, 1976, 307-313.

376. P. Ward. Un generateur de compilateurs a l'analyse descendante. Master's Thesis, Dept. d'Informatique, Universite de Montreal, 1975.

377. P. Ward. A top-down compiler writing system: Installation guide. Doc. de travail 78, Dept. d'Informatique, Universite de Montreal, 1979.

378. P. Ward. Un systeme d'ecriture de compilateurs a analyse syntaxique descendante. Doc. de travail 70, Dept. d'Informatique, Universite de Montreal, 1975.

379. P. Ward. A compiler writing system with top-down syntax analysis. User's manual. Universite de Montreal, Dept. d'Informatique, Publ.306, 1975.

380. S. Warshall and R.M. Shapiro. A general-purpose table-driven compiler. Proc. *AFIPS Spring Joint Computer Conf.,* Vol.25, 1964, 59-65.

381. K. Weiss. Deterministische indizierte Grammatiken. *Automata Theory and Formal Languages,* H. Brakhage (ed.), 2nd GI Conf., Kaiserslautern 1975, Lect. Notes in Comp. Sci. 33, 1975, 184-189.

382. K. Weiss. Deterministische indizierte Grammatiken. Doktorarbeit, TH Karlsruhe, Januar, 1976.

383. J.T. Webb. An implementation of Foster's syntax improving device for the ICL4100 computer. Royal Radar Establishment, Malvern, England, 1973, RRE-TN-774, BR 36160.

384. M. Wells and A. Denson. Direct execution of programming languages. *Computer Journal* 17 (1974), 130-134.

385. J. Welsh and M. McKeag. *Structured System Programming.* Prentice Hall International, London, 1980.

386. R.M. Wharton. Resolution of ambiguity in parsing. *Acta Informatica* 6 (1976), 387-395.

387. G. Whitney. An extended BNF for specifying the syntax of declarations. *AFIPS Spring Joint Computer Conf.,* 1969, 801-812.

388. R. Wilhelm, K. Ripken, J. Ciesinger, H. Ganzinger, W. Lahner and R. Nollmann. Design evaluation of the compiler generating system MUG1. Proc. 2nd Conf. on *Software Engineering,* San Francisco, 1976.

389. R. Wilhelm. LL- and LR- attributed grammars. In: *Programmiersprachen und Programmentwicklung.* H. Woessner (ed.), Informatik Fachberichte 53, GI-7.Fachtagung, Springer-Verlag, Berlin, 1982, 151-164.

390. N. Wirth. The design of a PASCAL compiler. *Software-Practice and Experience* 1 (1971), 309-333.

391. N. Wirth. *Compilerbau.* B.G. Teubner, Stuttgart, 1977.

392. D. Wood. A note on the Syntax Improving Device with improvements. Unpublished Memorandum, 1969.

393. D. Wood. A note on top-down deterministic languages. *BIT (Nordisk Tidskrift for Informationsbehandling)* 9 (1969), 387-399.

394. D. Wood. The normal form theorem - another proof. *Computer Journal* 12 (1969), 139-147.

395. D. Wood. A generalized normal form theorem for context-free grammars. *Computer Journal* 13 (1970), 272-277.

396. D. Wood. The theory of left factored languages. Parts I and II. *Computer Journal* 12 (1969), 349-356 and 13 (1970), 55-62.

397. D. Wood. A further note on top-down deterministic languages. *Computer Journal* 14 (1971), 396-403.

398. D. Wood. A factor theorem for subsets of a free monoid. *Information and Control* 21 (1972), 21-26.

399. D. Wood. Some remarks on the KH algorithm for s-grammars. *BIT (Nordisk Tidskrift for Informationsbehandling)* 13 (1973), 476-489.

400. D. Wood. A bibliography of top-down parsing. *SIGPLAN Notices* 13, Nr.2, February 1978, 71-76.

401. D. Wood. Lecture notes on top-down syntax analysis. *J. of the Computer Society of India* 8 (1978), 1-22.

402. P.M. Woodward. A note on Foster's syntax improving device. RRE Mem. No.2352, Royal Radar Establishment, Malvern, 1966.

403. H.P. Zeigler. Formal models for some standard features of programming languages. Proc. of ACM Symp. on *Theory of Computing*, 1969, 211-216.

404. S.A. Zhukov. Time complexity in the operation of a two-way parser. *Kibernetika* (Kiev) 1979, No.4, 105-111 (Russian); translated as *Cybernetics* 15 (1979), No.4, 552-558 (1980).

405. V.V. Zubenko. Simple pushdown storage automata and the equivalence problem in certain classes of LL(pi) grammars (in Russian). *Theory and Practice of Systems Programming* (Russian), Inst. Kibernet., Akad. Nauk Ukrain. SSR, Kiev, 1976, 60-76.

406. V.V. Zubenko, V.F. Kuzenko and S.S. Skil'njak. Syntactical definitions and the problem of reorientation (in Russian). *Akad. Nauk Ukrain. SSR*, Inst. Kibernet., Kiev, 1980.

3. LR-GRAMMARS AND PARSING: A BIBLIOGRAPHY

SURVEY OF THE LITERATURE

3.1. General and History

This bibliography contains references to papers and reports on LR-grammars and parsing. Other recently compiled bibliographies on parsing deal with:

- top-down parsing (see Section 2 of this Monograph and Wood[550])

- precedence relations (see Section 4 of this Monograph and Nijholt[364])

- error handling (Ciesinger[77])

- translator writing tools (Meijer and Nijholt[335])

According to LaLonde[295] LR(k) grammars "*.... are popular because the grammars describe a large class of programming languages, the parser constructing techniques take a "reasonable" amount of time, the parsing tables take a "reasonable" amount of space, the parsers are fast, i.e. operate in linear time, and they have excellent error detection properties.*" According to Aho[16] "*LR parsing is the single most promising parsing technique known at this time (1976).*"

All these nice properties were not immediately recognized when this class of grammars was introduced. LR(k) grammars (parsing from Left to right using Rightmost reductions and k symbols of lookahead) were introduced by Knuth[264] in 1965. Many of the formal properties of LR(k) grammars have already been discussed in this original paper. Later papers have been concerned with both more practical approaches of the parsing problem for LR(k) grammars and more formal treatment of the properties of LR(k) grammars and parsing. Classical theoretical problems are e.g. the relationships with other classes of grammars, decidability and equivalence problems and relationships with (deterministic) pushdown automata. LR(k) grammars can be considered as the largest class of grammars which can be parsed from left to right using a pushdown stack and a deterministic finite control. The class of LR(1) languages coincides with the class of deterministic languages (Ginsburg and Greibach[163]). There exist direct transformations from LR(k) to LR(1) grammars (cf. Mickunas[341] and Mickunas, Lancaster and Schneider[342]).

3.2. Properties of Grammars and Languages

LR(k) grammars are usually defined by introducing conditions on the rightmost derivations of a context-free grammar. Many, mostly slightly different, definitions of this type exist. See Geller and Harrison[154] for a survey and some basic consequences of the differences. Other definitions are possible, e.g. it is possible to put conditions on parsers which can be constructed for general context-free grammars (see e.g. Heilbrunner[205]). Definitions range from very formal (e.g. in terms of category theory, Hotz and Claus[215]) to operational. For practical reasons (parser size) various restrictions have been defined on the LR(k) definition. Often this is done in terms of properties of the state sets of the LR parser. In this way SLR(k) and LALR(k) grammars have been introduced.

Many classes of grammars have been defined between the LL(k) and LR(k) grammars. Deussen[108], Demers[91] and Brosgol[63] give unifying approaches for top-down and bottom-up parsing methods for these grammar classes. Another attempt to include such grammar classes in a general framework is in Nijholt[360]. LR(k) grammars can be transformed to more restricted classes of grammars. This is one of the theoretical areas where strict deterministic grammars (Harrison and Havel[196]) play an important role (cf. Moura[349]). LR(k) grammars can be transformed to certain types of bounded (right) context and precedence grammars. See Graham[173,175] and Gray and Harrison[181]. Some subclasses of the LR(k) grammars can be transformed to LL(k) grammars (cf. Soisalon-Soininen and Ukkonen[481] and Hammer[189]). The proof that each LL(k) grammar is an LR(k) grammar has developed from 'intuitively clear' (Knuth[265]) to formal. In [363] the many different proofs are compared. DeRemer[98] has first shown that the class of simple precedence grammars is included in the class of SLR(1) grammars.

The class of LR(1) languages coincides with the class of deterministic languages. Just as the proofs that each LL(k) grammar is an LR(k) grammar the proofs of this property illustrate the development and the use of mathematical proof techniques in formal language theory. Arguments and proofs yielding the result can be found in Knuth[264], Lehman[305], Hopcroft and Ullman[210,211], Aho and Ullman[13] and Harrison and Havel[197]. Especially in the latter paper the result is obtained in a rigorous way. The solution for the equivalence problem for deterministic languages has been approached bottom-up. That is, first the equivalence problem for regular languages was solved, then the equivalence problem for simple deterministic and LL(k) languages was shown to be decidable. Valiant[525] introduced new techniques which started new activities in this area. At this moment the results obtained by Oyamaguchi, Honda and Inagaki[376] and by Ukkonen[517] are the most general available. In this bibliography this research area is not covered.

3.3. Parsing and Parser Optimization

LR(k) grammars can be parsed in linear time. The number of states of an LR(k) parser can be exponential in the size of the grammar. Testing whether for a fixed value of k an arbitrary grammar is LR(k) can be done in deterministic polynomial time. In Hunt, Szymanski and Ullman[221] lower time bounds on the complexity of LR(k) and SLR(k) testing can be found. It is not known whether testing for the LALR(k) property can be done in polynomial time. Testing can be done by constructing the LALR(k) parser. However, this may take exponential time and space. In Ukkonen and Soisalon-Soininen[518] it is shown that LALR(k) testing is PSPACE-complete. Lower bounds on the sizes of LR-parsers are discussed in Pittl[403] and in Ukkonen[520].

Before the introduction of LR(k) grammars parsing methods have been introduced and used in the construction of compilers and compiler writing systems which resemble (restricted versions of) the LR parsing method. Moreover, some of these methods are suitable for grammars which can generate all deterministic languages. See e.g. Floyd[141] (1964) and Eickel et al[124] (1962; see also Schkolnick[450]). LR parsing is an example of a *shift-reduce* parsing method. The origins of such a method can be found in Floyd[140]. In Bauer[45] other remarks can be found on parsing methods in the early years of compiler construction. Since 1965 LR(k) (or SLR(k), LALR(k) etc.) grammars have been given for programming languages ranging from FORTRAN (Rauhauser[420], Russel[441]) to ADA (Persch et al[397], Wetherell [538] and others).

Apart from the references to papers and reports with theoretical results on LR(k) grammars, languages and parsing, references can be found to publications which deal with the construction of parsers (or compilers) and parser generating systems (or compiler writing systems) in which essential use is made of properties of LR(k) grammars and parsing. Some papers which have had much impact on the practical construction of LR parsers are by Korenjak[271], DeRemer[102], LaLonde, Lee and Horning[291], Aho and Johnson[14], Anderson, Eve and Horning[28] and Pager [386]. In some of these papers, and, moreover, in e.g. Purdom[408,410] and Horning and LaLonde[213] empirical results on the size and the speed of LR parsers are reported.

Parser efficiency can be increased by eliminating semantically irrelevant reductions from an LR parser. Moreover, it is possible to eliminate "error" and "don't care" entries from the tables which are constructed for an LR parser. One way to compress tables is by using lists. Such a method is used in the Yacc compiler writing system[241]. Among others, the following papers are concerned with parser optimization: Aho and Ullman[6,10], Anderson, Eve and Horning[28], Backhouse[39], Demers[90], Goos[169], Joliat[243,246], LaLonde[294], Makinouchi[326], Pager[385], Sekimo et al[457] and Soisalon-Soininen[482,484]. In Dencker et al[95] the algorithmic complexity of six compression methods for parser tables are compared and empirical results of their implementations for several programming languages are given.

3.4. More General Than Context-Free

Whenever a grammar is not LR(1), this does not necessarily mean that an LR(1) parsing method can not be used. Information which is available in the symbol table, rules concerning the precedence of symbols (operators) and other semantics can be embedded in the LR parser to resolve possible parsing conflicts. Aho, Johnson and Ullman[15], Tarhio[501] and Terry[505] discuss LR parsing for ambiguous grammars. Demers[89], Earley[123], Ruzicka[443] and Wharton[539] give some theoretical results in this area. Purdom and Brown[412], Kron et al[289] and Gillett and Leach[163] are concerned with the same problem. In the Yacc compiler writing system[241] the user has the possibility to add *disambiguating* rules to the syntax of the grammar for which an LR parser has to be constructed.

Less ad hoc generalizations of an LR parser are obtained if the parsing problem for more powerful classes of grammars is considered. LR-type grammars and parsing methods have been introduced for *indexed grammars* (Sebesta and Jones[455]; see also Parchmann et al[389]) and for *context-sensitive grammars* (cf. Walters[529]). Crowe[85] and Watt[530,531] consider the parsing problem for *affix grammars*. Just as in the case of context-free grammars, parsing methods for *two-level grammars* (van Wijngaarden grammars, W-grammars) have developed from the application of ad hoc ideas in the construction of a compiler (in this case for ALGOL 68) to formal parsing methods. See Birrell[52], Nadrchal et al[351] and Boom[56]. In Hunter et al[232] LL versus LR parsing is discussed. Meijer[334] comments on this paper. LR-type parsing of two-level grammars is treated in Ambler[22], Bowlden[62] and Wegner[535]. In Friede[150] restrictions on the definition of two-level grammars are introduced in order to obtain one-pass parsable grammars.

The problem of parsing and translation for Knuth's *attribute grammars* has become one of the more important topics in parsing theory. Among the papers dealing with this topic are those of Lewis, Rosenkrantz and Stearns[313], Jones and Madsen[247], Madsen[320], Milton[344], Raiha and Ukkonen[417], Rowland[439], Tarhio[500], Watt[532] and Wilhelm[541].

3.5. Automatic Parser Construction and Error-Handling

Automatic LR parser construction is almost always based on the following idea of DeRemer. LR(0) grammars are not always sufficient to describe programming language constructs. However, when we give an LR(0) parser the possibility of a look-ahead of one symbol then most conflicts can be resolved. Therefore automatic construction consists of first computing the LR(0) parser and then a method is used to incorporate a look-ahead of one symbol in this parser. This look-ahead computation has lead to the definitions of SLR(1), *comprehensive* LR(1), *not quite* LALR(1) and LALR(1) grammars. In Kristensen and Madsen[282] various methods (up to 1979) to compute LALR(k) look-ahead are compared. In DeRemer and Pennello[104] and in Fischer[136] other methods for computing look-ahead are presented.

Leinius[306], Peterson[398] and James[238] are concerned with error-correcting techniques which can be used in LR parsers. The techniques of Graham and Rhodes[175] have been used for SLR(k) grammars (see Druseikis and Ripley[116]) and for LALR(k) and LR(k) grammars (cf. Pennello and DeRemer[396] and Mickunas and Modrey[343]). Other recent papers on error correction for LR parsers are e.g. Tai[494], Dion and Fischer[112,113] Graham, Haley and Joy[178], Sippu and Soisalon-Soininen[470-472] and Roehrich[433]. Other references can be found in the bibliography and in Ciesinger[77]. A discussion on some error correcting techniques can be found in Gries[185]. An important issue in error correction theory is whether parsing is slowed down by the used technique.

It is impossible to start mentioning all the LR based parser generators which are in use today. Especially at West-German universities (e.g. Karlsruhe, Berlin, Dortmund and Muenchen) there have been successful activities in this area. The bibliography contains references to LR parser generators which have been developed in Belgium, Danmark, Finland, Norway, Italy, Japan, India, Korea, Canada and the U.S.A.

Johnson[241] describes the LALR(1) based parser generator Yacc which has been implemented on the UNIX system. Fischer[136] has developed an *incremental* LR parser constructor. That is, given an LR(1) parsing table corresponding to a grammar, and given a set of productions to be inserted into or deleted from the grammar, the parsing table is modified such that it corresponds to the new grammar.

Wetherell and Shannon[537] give an excellent account of ten years experience with an LR based parser generator. Raiha[418] reports experiences with the HLP compiler writing system. Obviously, any reader interested in the practical construction of LR parsers and parser generators can find a lot more examples in this bibliography.

REFERENCES

1. H. Abramson, W.F. Appelbe and M.S. Johnson. Assaulting the Tower of Babel: Experiences with a translator writing system. Technical Report 77-12, November 1977, Dept. of Computer Science, Univ. of British Columbia, Canada.

2. H.D. Abramson. Partial ordering of the syntax elements of a language. *BIT (Nordisk Tidskrift for Informationsbehandling)* 8 (1968), 1-7.

3. H.D. Abramson. The applicability matrix of a syntax-directed parsing processor. *BIT (Nordisk Tidskrift for Informationsbehandling)* 8 (1968), 253-261.

4. H.D. Abramson. A note on left-recursive rules and the partitioning of a recognition matrix for syntax-directed translation. *BIT (Nordisk Tidskrift for Informationsbehandling)* 10 (1975), 1-5.

5. A.V. Aho and J.D. Ullman. The care and feeding of LR(k) grammars. Proc. Third Annual Symp. on *Theory of Computing,* 1971.

6. A.V. Aho and J.D. Ullman. Optimization of LR(k) parsers. *J. Comput. System Sci.* 6 (1972), 573-602.

7. A.V. Aho and J.D. Ullman. LR(k) syntax directed translation. Unpublished Manuscript, Bell Laboratories, Murray Hill, N.J., 1972.

8. A.V. Aho and J.D. Ullman. A technique for speeding up LR(k) parsers. Proc. Fourth Annual Symp. on *Theory of Computing,* 1972.

9. A.V. Aho, P.J. Denning and J.D. Ullman. Weak and mixed strategy precedence parsing. *J. Assoc. Comput. Mach.* 19 (1972), 225-243.

10. A.V. Aho and J.D. Ullman. A technique for speeding up LR(k) parsers. *SIAM J. Computing* 2 (1973), 106-127.

11. A.V. Aho, S.C. Johnson and J.D. Ullman. Mechanical parser generation for ambiguous grammars. Conf. Record of the ACM Symp. on *Principles of Programming Languages,* Boston, 1973.

12. A.V. Aho and T.G. Peterson. A minimum distance error-correcting parser for context-free languages. *SIAM J. Computing* 1 (1972), 305-312.

13. A.V. Aho and J.D. Ullman. *The Theory of Parsing, Translation, and Compiling.* Vols. 1 and 2. Prentice Hall, Englewood Cliffs, N.J., 1972 and 1973.

14. A.V. Aho and S.C. Johnson. LR parsing. *Computing Surveys* 6 (1974), 99-124.

15. A.V. Aho, S.C. Johnson and J.D. Ullman. Deterministic parsing of ambiguous grammars. *Comm. ACM* 18 (1975), 441-452.

16. A.V. Aho. Language theory in compiler design. In: *Applied Computation Theory: Analysis, Design, Modeling.* R.T. Yeh (ed.), Prentice Hall, Englewood Cliffs, N.J., 1976.

17. A.V. Aho and J.D. Ullman. *Principles of Compiler Design.* Addison-Wesley, Reading, Mass., 1977.

18. A.V. Aho. Translator writing systems: Where do they stand? *Computer* 13 (1980), No.8, 9-14.

19. H.A. Alcabes. Syntactic error recovery in an LALR-parser. Master's Thesis, Dept. of Elect. Eng. and Comp. Sci., MIT, 1981.

20. V.E. Altman. A language implementation system. MAC TR-126, MIT, Cambridge, Mass., 1973.

21. A.L. Ambler. Nested LR(k) parsing using grammars of the Van Wijngaarden type. Ph.D. Thesis, Dept. of Computer Science, University of Wisconsin, Madison, 1973.

22. A.L. Ambler. Generating nested SLR(k) parsers. Proc. of the Eight Annual Princeton Conf. on *Information Sciences and Systems,* 1974, 307-310.

23. M. Ancona, G. Dodero and V. Gianuzzi. Algorithm for producing reduced LR(k) tables and parsers. Proc. of *AICA Congress,* Bari, Vol.2, 1979, 131-138.

24. M. Ancona and V. Gianuzzi. Implementation of reduced LR(k) tables when k > 1. Report No.47 of CNR Laboratory for Applied Mathematics. Genova, 1980.

25. M. Ancona and V. Gianuzzi. A new method for implementing LR(k) tables. *Information Processing Letters* 13 (1981), 171-176.

26. M. Ancona, G. Dodere and V. Gianuzzi. Building collections of LR(k) items with partial expansion of lookahead strings. *SIGPLAN Notices* 17, Nr.5, May 1982, 24-28.

27. T. Anderson. Syntactic analysis of LR(k) languages. Ph.D. Thesis, Univ. of Newcastle-Upon-Tyne, Northumberland, 1972.

28. T. Anderson, J. Eve and J.J. Horning. Efficient LR(1) parsers. *Acta Informatica* 2 (1973), 12-39.

29. T. Anderson and J.M. Rushby. An overview of sparse LR(k) parsers and their optimization. MRM/71, University of Newcastle-Upon-Tyne, Computing Laboratory, 1974.

30. S.O. Anderson and R.C. Backhouse. Least-cost error recovery in LR parsers: a basis. Heriot-Watt Univ., Edinburgh, Tech. Rep. Nr.7, 1979.

31. J. Aoe and Y. Yamamoto. Simplification of LR(1) parsers by GO TO graph. *Systems, Computers, Controls* 8 (1977), 68-76 (1979). Also: *Trans. Inst. Electron. & Comm. Eng. Jpn.* (Japan), Vol.E60, No.8, Aug. 1977, 444-445.

32. J. Aoe, Y. Yamamoto and R. Shimada. Practical method for optimizing LR(k) parser using matrix structure. *Trans. Inst. Electron. & Comm. Eng. Jpn.* Sect.E (Japan), Vol.E62, No.7, 521-521, 1979.

33. J. Aoe, Y. Yamamoto and R. Shimada. A method for speeding up LR(k) parsers using action patterns. *Trans. Inst. Electron. & Comm. Eng. Jpn.* Sect.E (Japan), Vol.E64, No.10, 688-690, 1981.

34. R.E. Asratyan. The expansion of the class of SLR(1) grammars. *Program. Comput. Software* 3 (1977), 397-398.

35. R.E. Asratyan. Expanding the class of SLR(1) grammars by determining symbol technique. *Program. Comput. Software* 6 (1980), Nr.2, 115-118.

36. A.V. Babichev. Modification of the LR(k) parser for parallel syntactic analysis. *Program. Comput. Software* 7 (1981), July-August, Nr.4, 199-205.

37. P. Bachman. Die Lokalisierung syntaktischer Fehler in kontextfreien Sprachen. *Elektronische Informationsverarbeitung und Kybernetik (EIK)* 9 (1973), 341-353.

38. S. Backes. Top-down syntax analysis and Floyd-Evans production language. Proc. of the *IFIP Congress 71,* North-Holland Publ. Co., Amsterdam, 1972, 504-508.

39. R.C. Backhouse. An alternative approach to the improvement of LR(k) parsers. *Acta Informatica* 6 (1976), 277-296.

40. R.C. Backhouse. *Syntax of Programming Languages: Theory and Practice.* Prentice Hall International, London, 1979.

41. Th.P. Baker. Extending look-ahead for LR parsers. *J. Comput. System Sci.* 22 (1981), 243-259.

42. J.P. Banatre. Structure d'un compilateur ALGOL 68. Thesis, Rennes, France, September 1974.

43. J.P. Banatre, F. Kerangueven and J.P. Routeau. Some aspects of compiler design and reliability. Proc. of the 5th Annual III Conf. *Implementation and Design of Algorithmic Languages,* J. Andre and J.-P. Banatre (eds.), 1977, 375-390.

44. W.A. Barrett and J.D. Couch. *Compiler Construction: Theory and Practice.* Science Research Associates, Inc., 1979.

45. F.L. Bauer. Historical remarks on compiler construction. In: *Compiler Construction: An Advanced Course.* F.L. Bauer and J. Eickel (eds.), Lect. Notes in Comp. Sci. 21, Springer-Verlag, Berlin, 1974, 603-621.

46. J.C. Beatty. Iteration theorems for the LL(k) languages. Ph.D. Thesis, Lawrence Livermore Laboratory, University of California, Livermore, 1977.

47. J.C. Beatty. On the relationship between the LL(1) and LR(1) grammars. Res. Report CS-79-36, University of Waterloo, Waterloo, Ontario, 1979.

48. J.C. Beatty. Two iteration theorems for the LL(k) languages. *Theoret. Comput. Sci.* 12 (1980), 193-228.

49. D.B. Benson and R.D. Jeffords. Parallel decomposition of LR(k) grammars. In: *Automata, Languages and Programming,* A. Salomaa and M. Steinby (eds.), Lect. Notes in Comp. Sci. 52, Springer-Verlag, Berlin, 1977, 76-86.

50. D.B. Benson and R.D. Jeffords. A vector encoding technique applicable to tabular parsing methods. Manuscript, 1977.

51. D.B. Benson. Some preservation properties of normal form grammars. *SIAM J. Computing* 6 (1977), 381-402.

52. A.D. Birrell. Problems in implementing ALGOL 68C. In: *ALGOL 68.* Proc. of the 1975 Int. Conf. on ALGOL 68, G.E. Hedrick (ed.), Oklahoma State University, Stillwater, 1975, 3-12.

53. M. Blattner. Structural similarity in context-free languages. *Information and Control* 30 (1976), 267-294.

54. J. Bodwin, L. Bradley, K. Kanda, D. Litle and U. Pleban. Experience with an experimental compiler generator based on denotational semantics. Proc. of the SIGPLAN'82 Symp. on *Compiler Construction*, 1982, 216-223.

55. B.I. Boiko. Two classes of grammars of inverse-quasirecursive type (Ukrainian). *Dopovidi Akad. Nauk Ukrain.*, RSR Ser. A, 1973, 675-677, 763. [MR 48#12904, 1974].

56. H. Boom. Textual management in an ALGOL 68 compiler. In: *ALGOL 68.* Proc. of the 1975 Int. Conf. on ALGOL 68, G.E. Hedrick (ed.), Oklahoma State University, Stillwater, 1975, 64-97.

57. R. Bornat. *Understanding and Writing Compilers.* MacMillan and Co., Ltd., London, 1979.

58. M. Bouckaert, A. Pirotte and M. Snelling. Improvements to Earley's context-free parser. In: *GI-3.Jahrestagung,* W. Brauer (ed.), Lect. Notes in Comp. Sci. 1, Springer-Verlag, Berlin, 1973, 104-112.

59. P. Boullier. Automatic syntactic error recovery for LR parsers. Proc. of the 5th Annual III Conf., *Implementation and Design of Algorithmic Languages,* J. Andre and J.-P. Banatre (eds.), 1977, 348-361.

60. P. Boullier. Automatic syntactic error recovery for LR parsers. Preliminary Document (Vol.2) of *State of the Art and Future Trends in Compilation,* Montpellier, 1978, 239-252.

61. H.J. Bowlden. Optimizing an SLR(k) parser. Manuscript, Westing House Research Laboratories, Pittsburgh, 1971.

62. H.J. Bowlden. Cascaded SLR(k) translators and ALGOL68. In: *Zweite Fachtagung ueber Programmiersprachen.* GI-Bericht Nr.4, Gesellschaft fuer Mathematik und Datenverarbeitung, 1972, 189-199.

63. B.M. Brosgol. Deterministic translation grammars. Ph.D. Thesis, TR-74, Harvard University, Cambridge, Mass., 1974.

64. B.M. Brosgol. Deterministic translation grammars. Proc. Eight Princeton Conf. on *Information Sciences and Systems,* 1974, 300-306.

65. B.M. Brosgol. A bottom-up approach to top-down parsing. Proc. of the 1977 Conf. on *Information Sciences and Systems,* The John Hopkins University, 1977, 195-201.

66. B.P. Buckles, B.C. Hodges and P. Hsia. A survey of compiler development aids. NASA TM X-3490, George C. Marshall Space Flight Center, Alabama, 1977.

67. W.F. Burger. BOBSW - A parser generator. SESL TR-7, December 1974, Department of Computer Science, The University of Texas, Austin.

68. C. Burgess and L. James. An indexed bibliography for LR grammars and parsers. *SIGPLAN Notices* 16, Nr. 8, August 1981, 14-26.

69. M. Burke and G.A. Fisher Jr. A practical method for syntactic error diagnosis and recovery. Proc. of the SIGPLAN'82 Symp. on *Compiler Construction,* 1982, 67-78.

70. A. Celentano. Parsing languages described by syntax graphs. *Int. Computing Symposium,* E. Morlet and D. Ribbens (eds.), 1977, 227-235.

71. A. Celentano. Incremental parsers. Report Nr.77-13, Istituto di Elettronica, Milano. Also: *Acta Informatica* 10 (1978), 307-321.

72. A. Celentano. An LR parsing technique for extended context-free grammars. Report 79-15, Istituto di Elettrotechnica ed Elettronica, Milano. Also: *Computer Languages* 6 (1981), 95-107.

73. P. Cerioli. An efficient parser for LR(k) grammars (in Italian). Thesis, T-IN/1981/4, Univ. of Genova, 1981.

74. Y.E. Cho. Simple left corner grammars. Seventh Annual Princeton Conf. on *Information Sciences and Systems,* 1973, 557-557.

75. T.W. Christopher. Implementation techniques for Earley algorithm. *ACM Comp. Sci. Conf.,* Washington, DC, 1975, p.40.

76. Chi Corporation. LIS language implementation system. Chi Corporation, Cleveland, Ohio, undated report.

77. J. Ciesinger. A bibliography of error-handling. *SIGPLAN Notices* 14, Nr.1, January 1979, 16-26.

78. CII Honeywell Bull. LALR(1) grammar for ADA. Unpublished computer listing, CII Honeywell Bull, 1979.

79. R.S. Cohen and K. Culik II. LR-regular grammars - an extension of LR(k) grammars. IEEE Conf. Record of 12th Annual Symp. on *Switching and Automata Theory*, 1971, 153-165.

80. J. Cohen et al. *A Compiler Generator*. Brandeis University, Waltham, Mass., 1972.

81. J. Cohen and M.S. Roth. Analysis of deterministic parsing algorithms. *Comm. ACM* 21 (1978), 448-458.

82. J. Cohen, T. Hickey and J. Katcoff. Upperbounds for speedup in parallel parsing. *J. Assoc. Comput. Mach.* 29 (1982), 408-428.

83. J.D. Cointment III. CCC - A mixed strategy compiler-compiler. Ph.D. Thesis, Southern Methodist University, Dallas, Texas, May 1972.

84. J. Crawford. Engineering a production code generator. Proc. of the SIGPLAN 82 Symp. on *Compiler Construction*, 1982, 205-215.

85. D. Crowe. Generating parsers for affix grammars. *Comm. ACM* 15 (1972), 728-734.

86. K. Culik and R. Cohen. LR-regular grammars - an extension of LR(k) grammars. *J. Comput. System Sci.* 7 (1973), 66-96.

87. S.E.R. De Carvalho. Design of interrelated lexical and syntactical analysers. Ph.D. Thesis, Univ. of Waterloo, Waterloo, Ontario.

88. A.J. Demers. Elimination of single productions and merging nonterminal symbols in LR(1) grammars. Princeton University Technical Report TR-127, 1973.

89. A.J. Demers. Skeletal LR parsing. Proc. 15th Annual Symp. on *Switching and Automata Theory*, 1974, 185-198.

90.   A.J. Demers. Elimination of single productions and merging nonterminal symbols of LR(1) grammars. *Computer Languages* 1 (1975), 105-119.

91.   A.J. Demers. Generalized left corner parsing. Conf. Record of the Fourth ACM Symp. on *Principles of Programming Languages,* 1977, 170-182.

92.   J. Demner. Strong LR(1) grammars (A modification of the DeRemer's parsing method). In: Report UVT 6/73/M, Technical University of Prague, 1973.

93.   J. Demner and J. Kral. Parsing as a subtask of compiling. In: *Mathematical Foundations of Computer Science,* J. Becvar (ed.), Lect. Notes in Comp. Sci. 32, Springer-Verlag, Berlin, 1975, 61-74.

94.   P. Dencker. Ein neues LALR System. Diplomarbeit, Universitaet Karlsruhe, Fakultaet fuer Informatik, 1977.

95.   P. Dencker, K. Duerre and J. Heuft. Optimization of parser tables for portable compilers. Int. Bericht Nr. 22/81, Universitaet Karlsruhe, Fakultaet fuer Informatik, November 1981.

96.   F.L. DeRemer. On the generation of parsers for BNF grammars: an algorithm. Report Nr. 276, Dept. of Computer Science, Univ. of Illinois, Urbana, 1968.

97.   F.L. DeRemer. Generating parsers for BNF grammars. Proc. 1969 *AFIPS Spring Joint Computer Conf.,* AFIPS Press, Montvale, N.J., 1969, 793-799.

98.   F.L. DeRemer. Practical translators for LR(k) languages. Ph.D. Thesis and Project MAC TR-65, MIT 1969.

99.   F.L. DeRemer. Simple LR(k) grammars: Definition and implementation. CEP Rep.2, 4, University of California at Santa Cruz, 1970.

100. F.L. DeRemer. Extended LR(k) grammars and their parsers. Manuscript, University of California at Santa Cruz, 1970.

101. F.L. DeRemer and W.R. LaLonde. A proposal to develop and implement an advanced translator writing system. Report Nr.75, University of California at Santa Cruz, 1971.

102. F.L. DeRemer. Simple LR(k) grammars. *Comm. ACM* 14 (1971), 453-460.

103. F.L. DeRemer. Lexical analysis. In: *Compiler Construction: An Advanced Course.* F.L. Bauer and J. Eickel (eds.), Lect. Notes in Comp. Sci. 21, Springer-Verlag, Berlin, 1974, 109-120.

104. F.L. DeRemer and T.J. Pennello. Efficient computation of LALR(1) look-ahead sets. ACM SIGPLAN Conf. on *Compiler Construction,* Denver, Colorado, 1979. *SIGPLAN Notices* 14 (1979), Nr.8, 176-187.

105. S. Desai. The design and implementation of an SLR parse table generator. Master's Thesis, San Francisco State University, San Francisco, California, 1980.

106. P. Deussen. A unified approach to the generation and the acception of formal languages. Int. Bericht Nr. 12/76, Fakultaet fuer Informatik, Universitaet Karlsruhe, 1976.

107. P. Deussen. Strategies in acceptors and their relation to LR(k)-/LL(k)-theories. Int. Bericht Nr. 8/77, Fakultaet fuer Informatik, Universitaet Karlsruhe, 1977.

108. P. Deussen. A unified approach to the generation and the acceptance of formal languages. *Acta Informatica* 9 (1978), 377-390.

109. P. Deussen. One abstract parsing algorithm for all kinds of parsers. In: *Automata, Languages and Programming,* H.A. Maurer (ed.), Lect. Notes in Comp. Sci. 71, Springer-Verlag, Berlin, 1979, 203-217.

110. P. Deussen. Nine classes of parsable languages obtained by refining one abstract accepting algorithm. Int. Bericht Nr. 1/78, Fakultaet fuer Informatik, Universitaet Karlsruhe, 1978.

111. E.-W. Dietrich. Parsing and syntactic error recovery for context-free grammars by means of coarse structures. In: *Automata, Languages and Programming,* A. Salomaa and M. Steinby (eds.), Lect. Notes in Comp. Sci. 52, Springer-Verlag, Berlin, 1977, 180-192.

112. B.A. Dion and C.N. Fischer. A least-cost error corrector for LR(1)-based parsers. Computer Sciences Dept., University of Wisconsin, Madison, Tech. Rep.333-WI, September 1978.

113. B.A. Dion and C.N. Fischer. An insertion-only error corrector for LR(1), LALR(1), SLR(1) parsers. Tech. Rep.315-WI, 1978, Computer Sciences Dept., University of Wisconsin, Madison, 1978.

114. F.C. Druseikis. SLR(1) parser generator. Dept. of Computer Science, University of Arizona, 1975.

115. F.C. Druseikis. Techniques for error recovery and error correction in simple LR(k) parsers. Tech. Report, Dept. of Computer Science, University of Arizona, 1976.

116. F.C. Druseikis and G.D. Ripley. Error recovery for simple LR(k) parsers. Proc. *ACM Annual Conference,* Houston, Texas, 1976, 396-400.

117. F.C. Druseikis and G.D. Ripley. Extended SLR(k) parsers for error recovery and repair. Dept. of Computer Science, University of Arizona, 1977.

118. K. Duerre, G. Goos and A. Schmidt. Darstellung der Tabellen von LR-Zerteilern. Manuscript, Universitaet Karlsruhe, Fakultaet fuer Informatik, August 1976.

119. J. Earley. Generating productions from BNF. Report, Carnegie Institute of Technology, 1964.

120. J.C. Earley. An LR(k) parsing algorithm. Carnegie Institute of Technology, Pittsburgh, Pa., 1967.

121. J. Earley. An efficient context-free parsing algorithm. Ph.D. Thesis, Carnegie-Mellon University, Pittsburgh, 1968.

122. J. Earley. An efficient context-free parsing algorithm. *Comm. ACM* 13 (1970), 94-102.

123. J. Earley. Ambiguity and precedence in syntax description. *Acta Informatica* 4 (1975), 183-192.

124. J. Eickel, M. Paul, F.L. Bauer and K. Samelson. A syntax controlled generator of formal language processors. Institut fuer Angew. Mathematik, Johannes Gutenberg Universitaet, Mainz, September 1962.

125. J. Eickel, M. Paul, F.L. Bauer and K. Samelson. A syntax controlled generator of formal language processors. *Comm. ACM* 6 (1963), 451-455.

126. J. Eickel. Generation of parsing algorithms for Chomsky type 2 languages. Bericht Nr.6401, Mathematisches Institut der Technischen Universitaet Muenchen, 1964.

127. N. El Djabri. Extending the LR parsing technique to some non-LR grammars. Princeton University Technical Report TR-121, 1973.

128. N. El Djabri. LR(1) parsers for precedence grammars. Comp. Sci. Lab., Dept. of Electr. Eng., Princeton University, 1973.

129. N. El Djabri. Parser optimization techniques. Ph.D. Thesis, Princeton University, 1974.

130. S.H. Eriksen, B.B. Jensen, B.B. Kristensen and O.L. Madsen. The BOBS-system. Computer Science Department, Aarhus University, 1973. (Revised version DAIMI PB-71, 1979 and February 1982).

131. J. Eve. On the recovery of LR(1) parsers from compacted parsing tables. MRM/68, University of Newcastle-upon-Tyne, Computing Laboratory, 1973.

132. J.A. Feldman and D. Gries. Translator writing systems. *Comm. ACM* 11 (1968), 77-113.

133. C.N. Fischer. On parsing context-free languages in parallel environments. Ph.D. Thesis, Tech. Rep. 75-237, Dept. of Computer Science, Cornell University, 1975.

134. C.N. Fischer, B.A. Dion and J. Mauney. A locally least-cost LR-error corrector. Tech. Report 363, Univ. of Wisconsin, 1979. To appear in *ACM Trans. Progr. Lang. Syst.*

135. G. Fischer. EXTRA - ein erweiterbarer Uebersetzer. *GI-9.Jahrestagung,* K.H. Boehling and P.P. Spies (eds.), Informatik Fachberichte 19, Springer-Verlag, Berlin, 1979, 240-251.

136. G. Fischer. Incremental LR(1) parser construction as an aid to syntactical extensibility. Ph.D. Thesis, Universitaet Dortmund, Abteilung Informatik, 1980.

137. D.A. Fisher. Control structures for programming languages. Ph.D. Thesis, Carnegie-Mellon University, June 1970.

138. G.A. Fisher and M. Weber. LALR(1) parsing for languages without reserved words. *SIGPLAN Notices* 14, November 1979, 26-30.

139. G. Fisher and M. Burke. Syntax error recovery in LALR(1) parsers. Report, Courant Institute, 1982.

140. R.W. Floyd. A descriptive language for symbol manipulation. *J. Assoc. Comput. Mach.* 8 (1961), 579-584.

141. R.W. Floyd. Bounded-context syntax analysis. *Comm. ACM* 7 (1964), 62-66.

142. R.W. Floyd. The syntax of programming languages - a survey. *IEEE Trans. on Electr. Computers,* Vol.EC-13, 1964, 346-353.

143. K.O. Franz. Ueber den Aufwand bei der LR(0) Analyse. Diplomarbeit, Saarbruecken, 1973.

144. H. Franzen, B. Hoffmann. B. Pohl and I. Schmiedecke. The EAGLE parser generator. An experimental step towards a practical compiler compiler using two-level grammars. Proc. of the 5th Annual III Conf. *Implementation and Design of Algorithmic Languages,* J. Andre and J.-P. Banatre (eds.), 1977, 397-420.

145. R.A. Fraley. Parse-ahead grammars: Theory and practice. Ph.D. Thesis, University of Wisconsin, Madison, 1975.

146. D. Friede. Ueber deterministische kontextfreie Sprachen und rekursiven Abstieg. IFI Berichte VI/78, Universitaet Hamburg, 1978.

147. D. Friede. Transition diagrams and strict deterministic grammars. In: 4th GI Conf. on *Theoretical Computer Science,* K. Weihrauch (ed.), Lect. Notes in Comp. Sci. 67, Springer-Verlag, Berlin, 1979, 113-123.

148. D. Friede. Partitioned LL(k) grammars. In: *Automata, Languages and Programming,* H. Maurer (ed.), Lect. Notes in Comp. Sci. 71, Springer-Verlag, Berlin, 1979, 245-255.

149. D. Friede. Partitioned context-free grammars. TUM-I8115, December 1981, Institut fuer Informatik, Technische Universitaet Muenchen.

150. D. Friede. On partitioned van Wijngaarden grammars (A first attempt). TUM-I8207, June 1982, Institut fuer Informatik, Technische Universitaet Muenchen.

151. M.M. Geller and M.A. Harrison. Strict deterministic versus LR(0) parsing. Conf. Record of the ACM Symp. on *Principles of Programming Languages,* 1973, 22-32.

152. M.M. Geller and M.A. Harrison. Characterizations of LR(0) languages. Conf. Record of the 14th Annual Symp. on *Switching and Automata Theory,* 1973, 103-108.

153. M.M. Geller. Compact parsers for deterministic languages. Ph.D. Thesis, Dept. of Computer Science, University of California, Berkeley, California, 1975.

154. M.M. Geller and M.A. Harrison. On LR(k) grammars and languages. *Theoret. Comput. Sci.* 4 (1977), 245-276.

155. M.M. Geller, H.B. Hunt III, T.G. Szymanski and J.D. Ullman. Economy of description by parsers, dpda's and pda's. *Theoret. Comput. Sci.* 4 (1977), 143-159.

156. M.M. Geller and M.A. Harrison. Characteristic parsing: A framework for producing compact deterministic parsers. *J. Comput. System Sci.* 14 (1977), 265-317 (Part I) and 318-343 (Part II).

157. M.M. Geller, M.A. Harrison and I.M. Havel. Normal forms of deterministic grammars. *Discrete Mathematics* 16 (1976), 313-321.

158. M.M. Geller, S.L. Graham and M.A. Harrison. Production prefix parsing. In: *Automata, Languages and Programming,* J. Loeckx (ed.), Lect. Notes in Comp. Sci. 14, Springer-Verlag, Berlin, 1974, 232-241.

159. C. Ghezzi and D. Mandrioli. A note on deterministic parsing from left to right and right to left. Report Nr.77-11. Istituto di Elettronica, Milano, 1977.

160. C. Ghezzi and D. Mandrioli. Augmenting parsers to support incrementality. Report Nr.77-6, Istituto di Elettronica, Milano, 1977.

161. C. Ghezzi and D. Mandrioli. Incremental parsing. Report Nr.76-15, Istituto di Elettronica, Milano. Also: *ACM Trans. Progr. Lang. Syst.* 1 (1979), 58-70.

162. R. Giegerich and R. Wilhelm. Implementierbarkeit attributierter Grammatiken. In: *GI-7.Jahrestagung,* H.J. Schneider (ed.), Informatik Fachberichte 10, Springer-Verlag, Berlin, 1977, 17-36.

163. W.D. Gillett and S. Leach. Embedding semantics in LR parser tables. *Software-Practice and Experience* 8 (1978), 731-753.

164. S. Ginsburg and S.A. Greibach. Deterministic context-free languages. *Information and Control* 9 (1965), 91-106.

165. S. Ginsburg, B. Leong, O. Mayer and D. Wotschke. On strict interpretations of grammar forms. *Math. Systems Theory* 12 (1979), 233-252.

166. R.S. Glanville. A machine independent algorithm for code generation and its use in retargetable compilers. Ph.D. Thesis, Computer Science Division, University of California, Berkeley, California, November 1977.

167. R.S. Glanville and S.L. Graham. A new method for compiler code generation. Conf. Record of the Fifth Annual ACM Symp. on *Principles of Programming Languages,* 1978, 231-240.

168. K.P. Golikov. Program of constructing a syntactical analyzer for simple LR(1) grammars (in Russian). In: *Obrabotka Simvol'nay Info. (Proc. Symbol. Info.),* Comp. CTR USSR Acad. Sci., Moscow, No.2, 1975, 85-89.

169. G. Goos. On eliminating chain-productions from LR-parsers. Manuscript, Universitaet Karlsruhe, Fakultaet fuer Informatik, May 1976.

170. G. Goos and G. Winterstein. Problems in compiling ADA. In: *Trends in Information Processing Systems,* A.J.W. Duijvestijn and P.C. Lockemann (eds.), Lect. Notes in Comp. Sci. 123, Springer-Verlag, Berlin, 1981, 173-199.

171. R.M. Graham. Bounded context translation. Proc. *AFIPS Spring Joint Computer Conf.,* Vol.25, Spartan, New York, 1964, 17-29.

172. S.L. Graham. Extended precedence languages, bounded right context languages and deterministic languages. IEEE Conf. Record of the 11th Annual Symp. on *Switching and Automata Theory,* 1970, 175-180.

173. S.L. Graham. Precedence languages and bounded right context languages. Ph.D. Thesis, Dept. of Computer Science, Stanford University, California, 1971.

174. S.L. Graham and S.P. Rhodes. Practical syntactic error recovery in compilers. Conf. Record of ACM Symp. on *Principles of Programming Languages,* 1973, 52-58.

175. S.L. Graham. On bounded right context languages and grammars. *SIAM J. Computing* 3 (1974), 224-254.

176. S.L. Graham and M.A. Harrison. Parsing of general context-free languages. In: *Advances in Computers.* Vol.14, M. Yovits and M. Rubinoff (eds.), Academic Press, New York, 1976, 77-185.

177. S.L. Graham, M.A. Harrison and W.L. Ruzzo. On-line context-free recognition in less than cubic time. Proc. of the Eight Annual ACM Symp. on *Theory of Computing,* 1976, 112-120.

178. S.L. Graham, C.B. Haley and W.N. Joy. Practical LR error recovery. ACM SIGPLAN Conf. on *Compiler Construction,* Denver, Colorado, 1979, *SIGPLAN Notices* 14 (1979), No.8, August, 168-175.

179. S.L. Graham, M.A. Harrison and W.L. Ruzzo. An improved context-free recognizer. *ACM Trans. Progr. Lang. Syst.* 2 (1980), 415-462.

180. J.N. Gray. Precedence parsers for programming languages. Ph.D. Thesis, Dept. of Computer Science, University of California, Berkeley, 1969.

181. J.N. Gray and M.A. Harrison. On the covering and reduction problems for context-free grammars. *J. Assoc. Comput. Mach.* 19 (1972), 675-698.

182. J.N. Gray and M.A. Harrison. Canonical precedence schemes. *J. Assoc. Comput. Mach.* 20 (1973), 214-234.

183. J.L. Gray. Implementation of a SLR(1) parsing algorithm. M.S. Thesis, Oklahoma State University, Stillwater, Oklahoma, 1976.

184. J.L. Gray. Implementation of a LALR(1) parsing algorithm. Computer Center Technical Note, Oklahoma State University, Stillwater, Oklahoma, 1976.

185. D. Gries. Error recovery and correction-An introduction to the literature. In: *Compiler Construction: An Advanced Course.* F.L. Bauer and J. Eickel (eds.), Lect. Notes in Comp. Sci. 21, Second Edition, Springer-Verlag, Berlin, 1976, 627-630.

186. M. Griffiths. Analyse deterministe et compilateurs. Doctoral Thesis, University of Grenoble, France, 1969.

187. M. Griffiths. Toute grammaire LL(k) est LR(k). *RAIRO Informatique Theorique* 8 (1974), 55-58.

188. F. Hadlock. Derived grammars with applications to syntactic analysis. Proc. 3rd Annual Princeton Conf. on *Information Sciences and Systems,* 1969, 413-416.

189. M.M. Hammer. A new grammatical transformation into deterministic top-down form. Mac TR-119, Ph.D. Thesis, Massachusetts Institute of Technology, 1974.

190. M.M. Hammer. A new grammatical transformation into LL(k) form. Proc. of the Sixth Annual ACM Symp. on *Theory of Computing,* 1974, 266-275.

191. M.A. Harrison. *Introduction to Formal Language Theory*. Addison-Wesley, Reading, Mass., 1978.

192. M.A. Harrison and I.M. Havel. On a family of deterministic grammars. In: *Automata, Languages and Programming,* M. Nivat (ed.), North-Holland Publ. Co., Amsterdam, 1973, 413-441.

193. M.A. Harrison. On the relation between grammars and automata. In: *Advances of Information Sciences* 4, J.T. Tou (ed.), 39-92, Plenum Press, New York, 1972.

194. M.A. Harrison and I.M. Havel. Real time strict deterministic languages. *SIAM J. Computing* 1 (1972), 333-349.

195. M.A. Harrison. On covers and precedence analysis. In: *GI-3.Jahrestagung,* W. Brauer (ed.), Lect. Notes in Comp. Sci. 1, Springer-Verlag, Berlin, 1973, 2-17.

196. M.A. Harrison and I.M. Havel. Strict deterministic grammars. *J. Comput. System Sci.* 7 (1973), 237-277.

197. M.A. Harrison and I.M. Havel. On the parsing of deterministic languages. *J. Assoc. Comput. Mach.* 21 (1974), 525-548.

198. M.A. Harrison and A. Yehudai. A hierarchy of deterministic languages. *J. Comput. System Sci.* 19 (1979), 63-78.

199. I.M. Havel. Strict deterministic languages. Ph.D. Thesis, University of California, Berkeley, California, 1971.

200. K. Hayashi. On the construction of LR(k) parsers. Proc. *ACM Annual Conf.,* 1971, 538-553.

201. S. Heilbrunner. Using item grammars to prove LR(k) theorems. Bericht Nr.7701, Fachbereich Informatik, Hochschule der Bundeswehr, Muenchen, 1978.

202. S. Heilbrunner. Definition, analysis and transformation of LC(k) grammars. Bericht Nr.7802, Fachbereich Informatik, Hochschule der Bundeswehr, Muenchen, 1978.

203. S. Heilbrunner. On the definition of ELR(k) and ELL(k) grammars. *Acta Informatica* 11 (1979), 169-176.

204. S. Heilbrunner. Zerteilungsverfahren mit unbeschraenkter Vorschau. Bericht Nr.8005, Fachbereich Informatik, Hochschule der Bundeswehr, Muenchen, 1980.

205. S. Heilbrunner. A parsing automata approach to LR theory. *Theoret. Comput. Sci.* 15 (1981), 117-157.

206. S. Heilbrunner. A metatheorem for undecidable properties of formal languages and its application to LRR and LLR grammars and languages. Manuscript, April 1981, Fachbereich Informatik, Hochschule der Bundeswehr, Muenchen.

207. S. Heilbrunner. Tests for the LR-, LL-, and LC-regular conditions. Manuscript, April 1981, Fachbereich Informatik, Hochschule der Bundeswehr, Muenchen.

208. J.B. Hext and P.S. Roberts. Syntax analysis by Domolki's algorithm. *Computer Journal* 13 (1970), 263-271.

209. M. Hilt. Fehlerbehandlung in LR-Parsergeneratoren. Diplomarbeit, Technische Universitaet, Muenchen, Institut fuer Informatik, 1977.

210. J.E. Hopcroft and J.D. Ullman. *Formal Languages and Their Relation to Automata.* Addison-Wesley, Reading, Mass., 1969.

211. J.E. Hopcroft and J.D. Ullman. *Introduction to Automata Theory, Languages and Computation.* Addison-Wesley, Reading, Mass., 1979.

212. J.J. Horning. Empirical comparison of LR(k) and precedence parsers. Memorandum, Comp. Syst. Res. Gr., University of Toronto, 1970.

213. J.J. Horning and W.R. LaLonde. Empirical comparison of LR(k) and precedence parsers. CSRG-1, University of Toronto, 1970. Also: *SIGPLAN Notices* 5, Nr.11, November 1970, 10-24.

214. J.J. Horning. LR grammars and analyzers. In: *Compiler Construction: An Advanced Course.* F.L. Bauer and J. Eickel (eds.), Lect. Notes in Comp. Sci. 21, Springer-Verlag, Berlin, 1974, 85-108.

215. G. Hotz and V. Claus. *Automatentheorie und Formale Sprachen. III. Formale Sprachen.* Bibliographisches Institut Mannheim, 1972.

216. G. Hotz. Normal-form transformations of context-free grammars. *Acta Cybernetica* 4 (1978), 65-84.

217. G. Hotz. LL(k)- und LR(k) Invarianz von kontextfreien Grammatiken unter einer Transformation auf Greibachnormalform. Fachbereich Informatik, Univ. des Saarlandes, Saarbruecken, 1978.

218. G. Hotz and R.J. Ross. LL(k)- und LR(k) Invarianz von kontextfreien Grammatiken unter einer Transformation auf Greibachnormalform. *Elektronische Informationsverarbeitung und Kybernetik (EIK)* 15 (1979), 73-86.

219. H.B. Hunt III, T.G. Szymanski and J.D. Ullman. Operations on sparse relations, with applications to grammar problems. Proc. of the Fifteenth Annual Symp. on *Switching and Automata Theory*, 1974, 127-132.

220. H.B. Hunt III and T.G. Szymanski. On the complexity of grammar and related problems. Proc. 7th Annual ACM Symp. on *Theory of Computing*, 1975, 54-65.

221. H.B. Hunt III, T.G. Szymanski and J.D. Ullman. On the complexity of LR(k) testing. *Comm. ACM* 18 (1975), 707-716.

222. H.B. Hunt III and T.G. Szymanski. Lower bounds and reductions between grammar problems. Techn. Report 216, Princeton University, August 1976.

223. H.B. Hunt III. A complexity theory of grammar problems. Conf. Record of the Third ACM Symp. on *Principles of Programming Languages*, 1976, 12-18.

224. H.B. Hunt III and T.G. Szymanski. Complexity meta theorems for context-free grammar problems. *J. Comput. System Sci.* 13 (1976), 318-334.

225. H.B. Hunt III and D.J. Rosenkrantz. Complexity of grammatical similarity relations. Proc. of a Conf. on *Theoretical Computer Science*, Waterloo, 1977, 139-145.

226. H.B. Hunt III, T.G. Szymanski and J.D. Ullman. Operations on sparse relations. *Comm. ACM* 20 (1977), 171-176.

227. H.B. Hunt III and T.G. Szymanski. Lower bounds and reductions between grammar problems. *J. Assoc. Comput. Mach.* 25 (1978), 32-51.

228. H.B. Hunt III and T.G. Szymanski. Corregendum to lower bounds and reduction between grammar problems. *J. Assoc. Comput. Mach.* 25 (1978), 687-688.

229. H. Hunt and D.J. Rosenkrantz. Efficient algorithms for structural similarity of grammars. Conf. Record of Seventh ACM Symp. on *Principles of Program-*

ming Languages, 1980, 213-219.

230. H.B. Hunt III. On the decidability of grammar problems. Technical Report 80-9, Dept. of Computer Science, State University of New York at Albany, 1980.

231. H.B. Hunt III. On the decidability of grammar problems. *J. Assoc. Comput. Mach.* 29 (1982), 429-447.

232. C.B. Hunter, A.D. McGettrick and R. Patel. LL versus LR parsing with illustrations from ALGOL 68. *SIGPLAN Notices* 12, Nr.6, June 1977, 49-53.

233. R. Hunter. *The Design and Construction of Compilers.* John Wiley and Sons, New York, 1981.

234. E.T. Irons. Structural connections in formal languages. *Comm. ACM* 7 (1964), 62-67.

235. S. Jaehnichen, C. Oeters and B. Willis. *Uebersetzerbau.* Friedr. Vieweg &-Sohn, Braunschweig, 1978.

236. S.K. Jain, M.L. Suthar, K. Kant and A.P. Mathur. An SLR(1) parser generating system. *J. Comput. Soc. India* 5 (1975), No.2, 3-7, 36.

237. B. Jankov. A method for translating and implementing programming languages. *Programmirovanie* 1980, No.1, 41-50, 95 (Russian); translated as *Program. Comput. Software* 6 (1980), No.1, 31-39.

238. L.R. James. A syntax directed error recovery method. Master's Thesis, Technical Report CSRG-13, Univ. of Toronto, 1972.

239. R.D. Jeffords. Algebraic decomposition of parsers. Ph.D. Thesis, Washington State University, Pullman, Wash., 1977.

240. H.J. Jeffrey. LR(k) parsing of strings in regular expressions. Ph.D. Thesis, University of Colorado, 1974.

241. S.C. Johnson. Yacc - Yet another compiler-compiler. CSTR 32, Bell Laboratories, Murray Hill, N.J., 1975. Also: *UNIX Programmer's Manual,* 7th edition, Vol. 2B, January 1979.

242. S.C. Johnson. Language development tools on the Unix system. *Computer* 13 (1980), No.8, 16-21.

243. M.L. Joliat. On the reduced matrix representation of LR(k) parsing tables. CSRG-28, Ph.D. Thesis, Univ. of Toronto, 1973.

244. M.L. Joliat. Practical minimization of LR(k) parser tables. *Information and Processing 74,* North-Holland Publ. Co., Amsterdam, 1974, 376-380.

245. M.L. Joliat. The BIGLALR(1) parser generator system. Bell-Northern Research Ltd., Report (613), 596-3293, January 1975.

246. M.L. Joliat. A simple technique for partial elimination of unit productions from LR(k) parsers. *IEEE Trans. Comput.* 27 (1976), 763-764.

247. N.D. Jones and M. Madsen. Attribute-influenced LR parsing. In: *Semantics Directed Compiler Generation,* N.D. Jones (ed.), Lect. Notes in Comp. Sci. 94, Springer-Verlag, Berlin, 1980.

248. K. Kaijiri, S. Uchinami and Y. Tezuka. A study of error correction and recovery for SLR(k) parsers (in Japanese). *Inf. Process. Soc. Jpn.* 18 (1977), No.3, 230-236.

249. F.P. Kaminger. Syntax definition by means of recursive graphs. IBM Laboratory Vienna, Techn. Report TR 25.078, 1968.

250. F.P. Kaminger. Generation, recognition and parsing of context-free languages by means of recursive graphs. *Computing* 11 (1973), 87-96.

251. G.A.M. Kamsteeg-Kemper. Analyse methode bottom-to-top en top-to-bottom gekombineerd (in Dutch). ALG. VGP 062, manuscript, Vakgroep Informatica, Twente University of Technology, 1972.

252. T. Kasami. An efficient recognition and syntax algorithm for context-free languages. Scientific Report AFCRL-65-758, Air Force Cambridge Research Lab., Bedford, Mass., 1965.

253. R. Kemp. Die Groesse des minimalen Analysators einer kontextfreien Grammatik. Lect. Notes in Economics and Mathematical Systems 78, Springer-Verlag, Berlin, 1972, 99-106.

254. R. Kemp. LR(k) Analysatoren. Technical Report A73/02, Dissertation. Mathematisches Institut und Institut fuer Angewandte Mathematik. Universitaet des Saarlandes, Saarbruecken, 1973.

255. R. Kemp. An estimation of the set of states of the minimal LR(0)-acceptor. In: *Automata, Languages and Programming,* M. Nivat (ed.), North-Holland Publ.

Co., Amsterdam, 1973, 563-574.

256. R. Kemp. Binaere und unaere Ausdruckssprachengrammatiken in Zusammenhang mit LR(k) Grammatiken. Diplomarbeit, Universitaet des Saarlandes, Saarbruecken, 1973.

257. R. Kemp. Minimierung von LR(k) Analysatoren. Technical Report A75/1, A75/2, Universitaet des Saarlandes, Saarbruecken, 1975.

258. R. Kemp. Die Groesse des zustandsminimalen LR(0)-Analysators. In: *Automata Theory and Formal Languages,* H. Brakhage (ed.), 2nd GI Conf., Kaiserlautern 1975, Lect. Notes in Comp. Sci. 33, Springer-Verlag, Berlin, 1975, 223-232.

259. R. Kemp. LR(0) grammars generated by a LR(0) parser. Report A79/18, Universitaet des Saarlandes, Saarbruecken, 1979.

260. R. Kemp. LR(0) grammars generated by LR(0) parsers. *Acta Informatica* 15 (1981), 265-280.

261. B.W. Kernighan and L.L. Cherry. A system for typesetting mathematics. In: *UNIX Programmer's Manual* (7th Edition, Vol.2B), January 1979.

262. K.N. King. Intercalation theorems for families of strict deterministic languages. Technical Report UCB-CS-KK-78-01, University of California, Berkeley, California, 1978.

263. K.N. King. Intercalation theorems for families of strict deterministic languages. *Theoret. Comput. Sci.* 10 (1980), 317-333.

264. D.E. Knuth. On the translation of languages from left to right. *Information and Control* 8 (1965), 607-639.

265. D.E. Knuth. Top-down syntax analysis. *Acta Informatica* 1 (1971), 79-110.

266. T. Komor. A certain property of modified factored grammars. *USSR Comput. Math. and Math. Phys.* 12 (1972), 319-325 (1973).

267. H. Kopp. Ueber den mittleren Zeitbedarf bei der LR(k)-Analyse kontextfreier Sprachen. In: *Automata Theory and Formal Languages,* H. Brakhage (ed.), 2nd GI Conf., Kaiserslautern 1975, Lect. Notes in Comp. Sci. 33, Springer-Verlag, Berlin, 1975, 57-63.

268. H. Kopp. Ueber die effizienz von LR(k) Analysatoren. Berichte des Fachbereichs Angewandte Mathematik und Informatik A 74/13, Universitaet des Saarlandes, Saarbruecken, 1974.

269. A.J. Korenjak and J.E. Hopcroft. Simple deterministic languages. IEEE Conf. Record of 7th Annual Symp. on *Switching and Automata Theory*, 1966, 34-46.

270. A.J. Korenjak. Deterministic language processing. Ph.D. Thesis, Princeton University, Princeton, N.J., September 1967.

271. A.J. Korenjak. Efficient LR(1) processor construction. Proc. of the First Annual ACM Symp. on *Theory of Computing*, 1969.

272. A.J. Korenjak. A practical method for constructing LR(k) processors. *Comm. ACM* 12 (1969), 613-623.

273. K. Koskimies. LALR(1) syntax analysis for the programming language Euclid (in Finnish). Internal Report C-1978-41, April 1978.

274. K. Koskimies and E. Soisalon-Soininen. On a method for optimizing LR parsers. *Int. J. Computer Math.* 7 (1979), 287-296.

275. J. Kral and J. Demner. A note on the number of states of the DeRemer's recognizer. Institute for Computation Techniques of the Czech Technical University, Praha, May 1972. Also: *Information Processing Letters* 2 (1973), 22-23.

276. J. Kral. Semi-top-down transition diagrams driven syntactic analysis. Part II. In: Report UVT 6/73/M, Technical University of Prague, 1973.

277. J. Kral. Bottom-up versus top-down syntax analysis revised. Report UVT 10/74, Technical University of Prague, 1974.

278. J. Kral. Semi-top-down transition diagrams driven syntactic analysis: Part 2. TR 11/74, Technical University of Prague, 1974.

279. J. Kral. Almost top-down analysis for generalized LR(k) grammars. In: *Methods of Algorithmic Language Implementation*, A. Ershov and C.H.A. Koster (eds.), Lect. Notes in Comp. Sci. 47, Springer-Verlag, Berlin, 1977, 149-172.

280. B.B. Kristensen, O.L. Madsen, B.B. Jensen and S.H. Eriksen. A short description of a translator writing system (BOBS-system). DAIMI PB-41, 1974.

281. B.B. Kristensen. Erkendelse og korrektion af syntax fejl under LR-parsing. Master's Thesis (in Danish), May 1974, DAIMI, University of Aarhus.

282. B.B. Kristensen and O.L. Madsen. Methods for computing LALR(k) lookahead. DAIMI PB-101, July 1979. Also: *ACM Trans. Progr. Lang. Syst.* 3 (1981), 60-82.

283. B.B. Kristensen and O.L. Madsen. Methods for LR(k) testing. (Informative diagnostics on LALR(k) conflicts.) DAIMI PB-106, November 1979.

284. B.B. Kristensen and O.L. Madsen. A general algorithm for solving a set of recursive equations (Exemplified by LR-theory). DAIMI PB-110, 1980.

285. B.B. Kristensen and O.L. Madsen. A practical state splitting algorithm for constructing LR-parsers. DAIMI PB-115, 1980.

286. B.B. Kristensen and O.L. Madsen. Diagnostics on LALR(k) conflicts based on a method for LR(k) testing. *BIT (Nordisk Tidskrift for Informationsbehandling)* 21 (1981), 270-293.

287. H.H. Kron. Modifizierter LR(k) Parser. Studienarbeit PU-S2, Computer Science Dept., Techn. Universitaet in Darmstadt, 1972.

288. H.H. Kron, H.-J. Hoffmann and G. Winkler. On an extension of SLR(k) parsers to LR(k) parsers with unbounded k. Research Report PU1R2/74, Computer Science Dept., Techn. Universitaet in Darmstadt, 1974.

289. H.H. Kron, H.-J. Hoffmann and G. Winkler. On a SLR(k) based parser system which accepts non-LR(k) grammars. In: *GI-4.Jahrestagung*, D. Siefkes (ed.), Lect. Notes in Comp. Sci. 26, Springer-Verlag, Berlin, 1975, 214-223.

290. W.R. LaLonde. An efficient LALR parser generator. Tech. Rep. CSRG-2, University of Toronto, M.A.Sc. Thesis, 1971.

291. W.R. LaLonde, E.S. Lee and J.J. Horning. An LALR(k) parser generator. Proc. *IFIP Congress 71*, North-Holland Publ. Co., Amsterdam, 1971, 153-157.

292. W.R. LaLonde. Practical LR analysis of regular right part grammars. Ph.D. Thesis, University of Waterloo, Waterloo, 1975.

293. W.R. LaLonde. On directly constructing LA(k)LR(m) parsers without chain reductions. Dept. of Systems Engineering and Computing Science, Carleton Univ., Ottawa, Tech. Report No. SE&CS 76-9, 1976.

294. W.R. LaLonde. On directly constructing LR(k) parsers without chain reductions. Conf. Record of the Third ACM Symp. on *Principles of Programming Languages,* 1976, 127-133.

295. W.R. LaLonde. Regular right part grammars and their parsers. *Comm. ACM* 20 (1977), 731-741.

296. W.R. LaLonde. Correctness proofs of an LR parser construction technique for regular right part grammars. Technical Report, Dept. of Systems Eng. and Computing Science, Carleton University, Ottawa, Ontario, 1978.

297. W.R. LaLonde. Constructing LR parsers for regular right part grammars. *Acta Informatica* 11 (1979), 177-193.

298. W.R. LaLonde. The construction of stack-controlling LR parsers for regular right part grammars. *ACM Trans. Program. Lang. Syst.* 3 (1981), 168-207.

299. B. Lang. Parallel non-deterministic bottom-up parsing. In: Proc. Int. *Symp. on Extensible Languages,* Grenoble 1971, *SIGPLAN Notices* 6, Nr.12, December 1971.

300. H. Langmaack. Application of regular canonical systems to grammars translatable from left to right. *Acta Informatica* 1 (1974), 111-114.

301. F. Laufkoetter. Ueberdeckung kontextfreier Grammatiken, insbesondere epsilon-freie Ueberdeckungen. Diplomarbeit, Lehrstuhl fuer Angewandte Mathematik insbesondere Informatik, Rhein.-Westf. Techn. Hochschule Aachen, 1979.

302. S.S. Lavrov and A.A. Ordjan. An extension of Knuth's algorithm for context-free language parsing. *Zh. Vychisl. Mat. i Mat. Fiz.* (Russian) 15, No.4, 1975, 1006-1019; translated in *USSR Comput. Math. and Math. Phys.* (GB).

303. S.A. Leach and W.D. Gillett. An extended syntax-directed translation scheme. UIUCDCS-R-76-795, Dept. of Computer Science, Univ. of Illinois at Urbana-Champaign, Urbana, Ill., 1976.

304. J.A.N. Lee, T.K. Bogert and H. Gigley. An annotated bibliography on syntax-directed translation. Technical Note, Publication No. TN/CS/00018, Computer Science Program, Univ. Massachusetts, Amherst, Mass., July 1970.

305. D. Lehman. LR(k) grammars and deterministic languages. *Israel J. Math.* 10 (1971), 526-530.

306. R. Leinius. Error detection and recovery for syntax directed compiler systems. Ph.D. Thesis, Univ. of Wisconsin, Madison, 1970.

307. B.L. Leong and D. Wotschke. The influence of productions on derivations and parsing. Conf. Record of the Third ACM Symp. on *Principles of Programming Languages,* 1976, 1-11.

308. J. Lewi, K. de Vlaminck, J. Huens and P. Mertens. SLS/1: A translator writing system. In: *GI-5. Jahrestagung,* J. Muehlbacher (ed.), Lect. Notes in Comp. Sci. 34, Springer-Verlag, Berlin, 1975, 627-641.

309. J. Lewi, K. de Vlaminck, J. Huens and M. Huijbrechts. *Methodology in Compiler Construction.* Part I: Concepts. North-Holland Publ. Co., Amsterdam, 1979: Part II: Implementation, 1982.

310. P.M. Lewis and R.E. Stearns. Syntax-directed transduction. IEEE Seventh Annual Symp. on *Switching and Automata Theory,* 1969, 21-35.

311. P.M. Lewis and R.E. Stearns. Syntax directed transduction. *J. Assoc. Comput. Mach.* 15 (1968), 464-488.

312. P.M. Lewis, D.J. Rosenkrantz and R.E. Stearns. Attributed translation. Proc. 5th Annual ACM Symp. on *Theory of Computing,* 1973, 160-171.

313. P.M. Lewis, D.J. Rosenkrantz and R.E. Stearns. Attributed translations. *J. Comput. System Sci.* 9 (1974), 270-304.

314. G. Lindstrom. The design of parsers for incremental language processors. Proc. 2nd Annual ACM Symp. on *Theory of Computing,* 1970, 81-91.

315. J. Loeckx. An algorithm for the construction of bounded-context parsers. *Comm. ACM* 13 (1970), 297-307.

316. D.B. Lomet. The construction of efficient deterministic language processors. Ph.D. Thesis, Univ. of Pennsylvania, Philadelphia, 1969.

317. D.B. Lomet. A formalization of transition diagram systems. *J. Assoc. Comput. Mach.* 20 (1973), 235-257.

318. D.B. Lomet. Automatic generation of multiple exit parsing subroutines. In: *Automata, Languages and Programming,* J. Loeckx (ed.), Lect. Notes in Comp. Sci. 14, Springer-Verlag, Berlin, 1974, 214-231.

319. H. Ludwigs. A LR-like analyzer algorithm for graphs. In: *GI-10.Jahrestagung,* R. Wilhelm (ed.), Informatik Fachberichte 33, Springer-Verlag, Berlin, 1980, 321-335.

320. M. Madsen. Parsing attribute grammars. Doctoral Thesis, Dept. of Computer Science, University of Aarhus, Denmark, February 1980.

321. M. Madsen and N.D. Jones. Letting the attributes influence the parsing. Undated manuscript.

322. O.L. Madsen and B.B. Kristensen. On extended context-free grammars and LR- parsing. DAIMI PB-53, 1975, University of Aarhus, Denmark.

323. O.L. Madsen and B.B. Kristensen. LR-parsing of extended context-free grammars. *Acta Informatica* 7 (1976), 61-73.

324. E. Makinen. On the epsilon-free covering of LR(k) grammars. Report A52, April 1981, Dept. of Mathematical Sciences, Univ. of Tampere, Finland.

325. A. Makinouchi. Another practical method of analyser construction for LR(k) languages - an extension of SLR(k) (in Japanese). *Inf. Process. Soc. Jpn.* 17 (1976), No.8, 729-735.

326. A. Makinouchi. On single production elimination in simple LR(k) environment. *J. Inform. Process.* 1 (1978), 76-80.

327. K. Matsuoka. Context-sensitive LR(k) parsers. *Trans. Inst. Electron. &- Comm. Eng. Jpn.* Sect.E (Japan), Vol.E64, p.691, 1981.

328. J. Mauney and C.N. Fischer. A forward move algorithm for LL and LR parsers. Proc. of the SIGPLAN'82 Symp. on *Compiler Construction,* 1982, 79-87.

329. O. Mayer. *Syntaxanalyse.* Bibliographisches Institut Mannheim, 1978.

330. O. Mayer. A framework for producing deterministic canonical bottom-up parsers. In: *Mathematical Foundations of Computer Science,* J. Winkowski (ed.), Lect. Notes in Comp. Sci. 64, Springer-Verlag, Berlin, 1978, 355-363.

331. O. Mayer. On determinstic canonical bottom-up parsing. *Information and Control* 43 (1979), 280-303.

332. G.T. McGruther. An approach to automatic syntax error detection, recovery and correction for LR(k) grammars. Naval Postgraduate School, Monterey,

California, Master's Thesis, 1972.

333. W.M. McKeeman, J.J. Horning and D.B. Wortman. *A Compiler Generator.* Prentice Hall, Englewood Cliffs, N.J., 1970.

334. R.W. Meijer. A note on "LL versus LR parsing with illustrations from ALGOL 68". *SIGPLAN Notices* 12, Nr. 12, December 1977, 30-32.

335. H. Meijer and A. Nijholt. Translator writing tools since 1970: A selective bibliography. *SIGPLAN Notices,* 1982, to appear.

336. M.D. Mickunas. Techniques for compresssing bounded-context acceptors. Ph.D. Thesis, Purdue University, West Lafayette, In., 1973.

337. M.D. Mickunas and V.B. Schneider. A comparison of weak precedence, LALR, and bounded context parsing techniques. Manuscript, Purdue University, West LaFayette, In., 1973.

338. M.D. Mickunas. Strong covering problem for LR(k) grammars. PB-230 304/ 8GA, University of Illinois, Dept. of Computer Science, Urbana, 1973.

339. M.D. Mickunas and V.B. Schneider. On the ability to cover LR(k) grammars with LR(1), SLR(1) and (1,1) bounded context grammars. IEEE Conf. Record of 14th Annual Symp. on *Switching and Automata Theory,* 1973, 109-121.

340. M.D. Mickunas and V.B. Schneider. A parser generating system for constructing compressed compiler. *Comm. ACM* 16 (1973), 669-676.

341. M.D. Mickunas. On the complete covering problem for LR(k) grammars. *J. Assoc. Comput. Mach.* 23 (1976), 17-30.

342. M.D. Mickunas, R.L. Lancaster and V.B. Schneider. Transforming LR(k) grammars to LR(1), SLR(1) and (1,1) bounded-right-context grammars. *J. Assoc. Comput. Mach.* 23 (1976), 511-533.

343. M.D. Mickunas and J.D. Modry. Automatic error recovery for LR parsers. *Comm. ACM* 21 (1978), 459-465.

344. D.R. Milton. Syntactic specification and analysis using attribute grammars. Ph.D. Thesis, Computer Science Dept., Tech. Report #304, University of Wisconsin-Madison, 1977.

345. W. Mitteneder. Effizienter LR(1)-Parser. Diplomarbeit PU-S12, Comp. Sci. Dept., Technische Universitaet in Darmstadt, 1972.

346. J.A. Modrey. Syntactic error recovery for LR parsers. M.Sc. Thesis, Univ. of Illinois, 1976.

347. K.R. Moll. Left context precedence grammars. *Acta Informatica* 14 (1980), 317-336.

348. G. Molnar. Language independent error handling in a LALR analyser (in Hungarian). *Inf. Elektron.* (Hungary) 17 (1982), 46-51.

349. A. Moura. Syntactic equivalence of grammar classes. Ph.D. Thesis, University of California, Berkeley, September, 1980.

350. J.E. Musinski. Lookahead recall error recovery for LALR parsers. *SIGPLAN Notices* 12, Nr.10, October 1977, 48-60.

351. J. Nadrchal, J. Kral, I. Sklenar, V. Kriz and J. Moudry. Error recovery and other features of the ALGOL 68 Prague implementation. In: *ALGOL 68. Proc. of the 1975 Int. Conf. on ALGOL 68*. G.E. Hedrick (ed.), Oklahoma State University, Stillwater, 1975, 52-57.

352. A. Nijholt. On the covering of parsable grammars. *J. Comput. System Sci.* 15 (1977), 99-110.

353. A. Nijholt. Simple chain grammars. In: *Automata, Languages and Programming,* A. Salomaa and M. Steinby (eds.), Lect. Notes in Comp. Sci. 52, Springer-Verlag, Berlin, 1977, 352-364.

354. A. Nijholt. On the parsing and covering of simple chain grammars. In: *Automata, Languages and Programming,* G. Ausiello and C. Bohm (eds.), Lect. Notes in Comp. Sci. 62, Springer-Verlag, Berlin, 1978, 330-344.

355. A. Nijholt. Strict deterministic grammars and Greibach normal form. *Elektronische Informationsverarbeitung und Kybernetik (EIK)* 15 (1979), 395-401.

356. A. Nijholt. Simple chain grammars and languages. *Theoret. Comput. Sci.* 9 (1979), 287-309.

357. A. Nijholt and E. Soisalon-Soininen. Ch(k) grammars: A characterization of LL(k) languages. In: *Mathematical Foundations of Computer Science,* J. Becvar (ed.), Lect. Notes in Comp. Sci. 74, Springer-Verlag, Berlin, 1979, 390-397.

358. A. Nijholt. *Context-Free Grammars: Covers, Normal Forms, and Parsing.* Lect. Notes in Comp. Sci. 93, Springer-Verlag, Berlin, 1980.

359. A. Nijholt. A framework for classes of grammars between the LL(k) and LR(k) grammars. CSTR-No. 80-CS-25, McMaster University, Hamilton, Ontario, 1980.

360. A. Nijholt. Parsing strategies: A concise survey. In: *Mathematical Foundations of Computer Science.* M. Chytil and J. Gruska (eds.), Lect. Notes in Comp. Sci. 118, Springer-Verlag, Berlin, 1981, 103-120.

361. A. Nijholt. The equivalence problem for LL- and LR- regular grammars. In: *Fundamentals of Computation Theory,* F. Gecseg (ed.), Lect. Notes in Comp. Sci. 117, Springer-Verlag, Berlin, 1981, 291-300.

362. A. Nijholt. The equivalence problem for LL- and LR- regular grammars. *J. Comput. System Sci.* 24 (1982), 149-161.

363. A. Nijholt. On the relationship between the LL(k) and LR(k) grammars. Report IR-34, Katholieke Universiteit Nijmegen, 1982. To appear in *Information Processing Letters.*

364. A. Nijholt. Precedence relations: A bibliography. *SIGACT News,* Vol.14, Nr.2, Spring 1982, 9-19.

365. A. Nijholt and J. Pittl. A general scheme for some deterministically parsable grammars and their strong equivalents. Report IR-38, Katholieke Universiteit Nijmegen, August 1982. To appear in Proceedings of the 6th GI-Conf. on *Theoretical Informatics,* Dortmund, 1983.

366. O. Nurmi. Testing the LR(k) and SLR(k) conditions in the compiler writing system HLP (in Finnish). Internal Report C-1979-82, June 1979.

367. O. Nurmi, M. Sarjakoski and S. Sippu. The HLP'84 project. Manuscript, Dept. of Computer Science, University of Helsinki, March 1982.

368. O. Nurmi, M. Sarjakoski and S. Sippu. System HLP 84 - A tool for compiler writing. Manuscript, Dept. of Computer Science, University of Helsinki, May 1982.

369. H.G. Oberhauser. Speicherplatzeffiziente Implementierung eines LR(1)-parsergenerators. In: *Compiler-Compiler.* W. Henhapl (ed.), 3. GI-Fachgespraech, Muenchen, March 1982, 3-21.

370. W.F. Ogden. Intercalation theorems for pushdown store and stack languages. Ph.D. Thesis, Stanford University, Palo Alto, California, 1968.

371. M.F. O'Hare. Modificaton of the LR(k) parsing technique to include automatic syntactic error recovery. Thesis, University of California, Santa Cruz, 1976.

372. K. Omaki, A. Maruoka and M. Kimura. Non-crossing relation on LR grammars. *Trans. Inst. Electron. & Comm. Eng. Jpn.* Sect.E, Vol.E62, No.1, 832-833, 1979.

373. J. Okhura, S. Uchinami and Y. Tezuka. A method for the reduction of the LR(k) parsers. *Trans. Inst. Electron. & Comm. Eng. Jpn.* Sect.E (Japan), Vol.E60, No.1, Jan. 1977, p.63.

374. A.A. Ordjan. GP- and ELR(1)-languages (Russian). *Z. Vycisl. Mat. Fiz.* 15 (1975), 1289-1297, 1362. [MR 53#12108, 1977].

375. A.A. Ordjan. The total precedence languages and the ELR(1) languages (in Russian). *Zh. Vychisl. Mat. i Mat. Fiz.* (USSR) 15 (1975), No.5, 1289-1297; English translation in: *USSR Comput. Math. and Math. Phys.* (GB).

376. M. Oyamaguchi, N. Honda and Y. Inaguki. The equivalence problem for real-time strict deterministic languages. *Information and Control* 45 (1980), 90-115.

377. D. Pager. A solution to an open problem by Knuth. *Information and Control* 17 (1970), 462-473.

378. D. Pager. On the incremental approach to left-to-right parsing. TR PE 238, Information Sciences Program, University of Hawaii, 1972.

379. D. Pager. A fast left-to-right parser for context-free grammars. TR PE 240, Information Sciences Program, University of Hawaii, 1972.

380. D. Pager. A compaction algorithm for combining the symbol-action lists of an LR(k) parser. Univ. of Hawaii, Info. Sciences Program, Tech. Report No. PE 259, July 1972.

381. D. Pager. Efficient programming techniques for LR(k) parsing. Proc. Seventh Annual Princeton Conf. on *Information Sciences and Systems,* 1973.

382. D. Pager. The lane tracing algorithm for constructing LR(k) parsers. Proc. of the Fifth Annual ACM Symp. on *Theory of Computing,* 1973, 172-181.

383. D. Pager. On eliminating unit productions from LR(k) parsers. In: *Automata, Languages and Programming,* J. Loeckx (ed.), Lect. Notes in Comp. Sci. 14, Springer-Verlag, Berlin, 1974, 627-638.

384. D. Pager. Left-to-right parsing techniques. *Eurocomp Conf.,* Brunel University, May 1974, Data Proc.

385. D. Pager. Eliminating unit productions from LR parsers. *Acta Informatica* 9 (1977), 31-59.

386. D. Pager. A practical general method for constructing LR(k) parsers. *Acta Informatica* 7 (1977), 249-268.

387. D. Pager. The lane-tracing algorithm for constructing LR(k) parsers and ways of enchancing its efficiency. *Information Sciences* 12 (1977), 19-42.

388. C. Pair. Toute grammaire LL(k) est LR(k) (suite). *RAIRO Informatique Theorique* 8 (1974), 55-58.

389. R. Parchman, J. Duske and J. Specht. On deterministic indexed languages. *Information and Control* 45 (1980), 48-67.

390. J.C.H. Park, C.H. Chang, K.M. Choe, S.M. Oh and J.W. Yoo. PGS81 - An efficient LR parser generating system. CSRC Technical Report TR81-0001-0, Computer Science Research Center, Korea Advanced Institute of Science and Technology; Seoul, Korea, July 1981.

391. J.C.H. Park. A new LALR formalism. *SIGPLAN Notices* 17, Nr.7, July 1982, 47-61.

392. M. Paul. A general processor for certain formal languages. Proc. Symp. on *Symbolic Languages in Data Processing,* Rome 1962, Gordon and Breach, New York, 1962.

393. I.E. Pedanov and A.S. Shumei. Extensions of the class of LR(0) grammars. *Automat. Remote Control* 34, No.11, November 1973, 1844-1849.

394. T.J. Pennello. Error recovery for LR parsers. M.Sc. Thesis, Information Sciences, University of California, Santa Cruz, 1977.

395. T.J. Pennello and F. DeRemer. Practical error recovery for LR parsers. Information Sciences, Tech. Rep.78-1-002, University of California, Santa Cruz, 1977.

396. T.J. Pennello and F.L. DeRemer. A forward move algorithm for LR error recovery. Conf. record of the Fifth Annual ACM Symp. on *Principles of Programming Languages,* 1978, 231-240.

397. G. Persch, G. Winterstein, S. Drossopoulou and M. Dausmann. An LALR(1) grammar for (Revised) ADA. *SIGPLAN Notices* 16, Nr.3, March 1981, 85-98.

398. T.G. Peterson. Syntax error detection, correction and recovery in parsers. Ph.D. Thesis, Stevens Institute of Technology, Hoboken, N.J., May 1972.

399. J. Pittl. Characteristic parsing of LLP(k) grammars. Thesis (in Czech), Charles University, Prague, 1978.

400. J. Pittl. Exponential optimization for the LLP(k) parsing method. In: *Mathematical Foundations of Computer Science,* J. Gruska (ed.), Lect. Notes in Comp. Sci. 53, Springer-Verlag, Berlin, 1977, 435-442.

401. J. Pittl. On LLP(k) grammars and languages. *Theoret. Comput. Sci.* 16 (1981), 149-175.

402. J. Pittl. On LLP(k) parsers. *J. Comput. System Sci.* 24 (1982), 36-68.

403. J. Pittl. Negative results on the size of deterministic right parsers. In: *Mathematical Foundations of Computer Science,* J. Gruska and M. Chytil (eds.), Lect. Notes in Comp. Sci. 118, Springer-Verlag, Berlin, 1981, 442-451.

404. W. Polak. *Compiler Specification and Verification.* Lect. Notes in Comp. Sci. 124, Springer-Verlag, Berlin, 1981.

405. B.W. Pollack (ed.). *Compiler Techniques.* Auerbach Publishers, Philadelphia, 1972.

406. G. Poonen. Error recovery for LR(k) parsers. In: *Information Processing 77,* B. Gilchrist (ed.), North-Holland Publ. Co., Amsterdam, 1977, 529-533.

407. V.N. Popolitov. Detection and correction of syntactical errors in analysis of LR(k) grammars (in Russian). In: *Control of Technical and Organizational Systems by Application of Computer Technology* (Russian), "Nauka", Moscow, 1979, 79-83; 227.

408. P. Purdom. The size of LR(0) machines. Technical Report No.2, Computer Science Department, Indiana University, undated.

409. P. Purdom. A sentence generator for testing parsers. *BIT (Nordisk Tidskrift for Informationsbehandling)* 12 (1972), 366-375. See also: C. Bohm, Review 25.940, *Computing Reviews 14 (1973).*

410. P. Purdom. The size of LALR(1) parsers. *BIT (Nordisk Tidskrift for Informationsbehandling)* 14 (1974), 326-337.

411. P. Purdom and C. Brown. Semantic routines and LR(k) parsers. Techn. Report No.83, Computer Science Department, Indiana University, 1979.

412. P. Purdom Jr. and C.A. Brown. Semantic routines and LR(k) parsers. *Acta Informatica* 14 (1980), 299-315.

413. P. Purdom Jr. and C.A. Brown. Parsing extended LR(k) grammars. *Acta Informatica* 15 (1981), 115-127.

414. A.B. Pyster. *Compiler Design and Construction.* Van Nostrand Reinhold, 1980.

415. K.-J. Raiha and M. Saarinen. Developments in compiler writing systems. In: *GI-6.Jahrestagung,* E.J. Neuhold (ed.), Informatik Fachberichte 5, Springer-Verlag, Berlin, 1976, 164-178.

416. K.-J. Raiha, M. Saarinen, E. Soisalon-Soininen and M. Tienari. The compiler writing system HLP (Helsinki Language Processor). Report A-1978-2, Dept. of Computer Science, University of Helsinki, 1978.

417. K.-J. Raiha and E. Ukkonen. Balancing syntactic and semantic power in compiler specification. In: *Information Processing 80,* S.H. Lavington (ed.), North-Holland Publ. Co., Amsterdam, 1980, 65-70.

418. K.-J. Raiha. Experiences with the compiler writing system HLP. In: *Semantics Directed Compiler Generation,* N.D. Jones (ed.), Lect. Notes in Comp. Sci. 94, Springer-Verlag, Berlin, 1980, 350-362.

419. D.R. Ramer. Construction of LR(k) parsers with applications to ALGOL 68, M.Sc. Thesis, Dept. of Computer Science, University of British Columbia, 1973.

420. R.C. Rauhauser. An LALR(1) parser grammar for FORTRAN. Manuscript, Dept. of Computer Science, Colorado University, Boulder, 1978.

421. P. Rechenberg. Practical bounded-right-context analysis with small storage. *Elektronische Rechenanlagen* 18 (1976), No.1, 5-14.

422. J. Reichardt. Analysierbarkeit und Normalformentransformation kontextfreier Grammatiken. TI 1/79, University of Darmstadt, 1979.

423. K. Rekdal and T. Wessel. Generator for SLR(1)-analysatorer (in Norwegian). Report, RUNIT, August 1972.

424. K. Rekdal. Practical construction of syntax-directed translators. In: *Information Processing 74*, North-Holland Publ. Co., Amsterdam, 1974, 372-375.

425. J.P. Rethore. Automates a piles communicantes. These 3e cycle, Department of Computer Science, University of Lille, 1975.

426. G. Revesz. Unilateral context-sensitive grammars and left to right parsing. *J. Comput. System Sci.* 5 (1971), 337-352.

427. S.P. Rhodes. Practical syntactic error recovery for programming languages. Tech. Report No.15, Computer Science Division, University of California, Berkeley, 1973.

428. H. Richter. Syntaxfehlerbehandlung ohne Korrekturversuche (Syntax error recovery without correction attempts). Ph.D. Thesis, University of Munich, LRZ-Bericht Nr. 8204/1, April 1982.

429. A. Robertson, M. Goto and G.E. Hedrick. Grammars for ALGOL 68 format denotations and the transput facilities of the OSU ALGOL 68 compiler. Proc. of the 5th Annual III Conf. *Implementation and Design of Algorithmic Languages,* J. Andre and J.-P. Banatre (eds.), 1977, 222-252.

430. M.A. Rogers and L.M. Meyers. An adaptation of the ADA language for machine generated compilers. AD-A097 292/7, Naval Postgraduate School, Monterey, CA, 1977.

431. J. Roehrich. Syntax error recovery in LR parsers. In: *Programmiersprachen,* GI-4.Fachtagung, H.J. Schneider and M. Nagl (eds.), Informatik Fachberichte 1, Springer-Verlag, Berlin, 1976, 175-184.

432. J. Roehrich. Automatic construction of error correcting parsers. Dissertation, Int. Bericht Nr.8, Fakultaet fuer Informatik, Universitaet Karlsruhe, 1977.

433. J. Roehrich. Methods for the automatic construction of error correcting parsers. *Acta Informatica* 13 (1980), 115-139.

434. S. Rosen (ed.). *Programming Systems and Languages.* McGraw-Hill, New York, 1967.

435. M. Rosendahl. Zur Analysierung gewisser Klassen formaler Sprachen durch von links un rechts lesende Automaten. In: *Automatentheorie und Formale Sprachen*. J. Doerr and G. Hotz (eds.), Tagung Oberwolfach 1969, Bibliographisches Institut Mannheim, 1970, 273-289.

436. D.J. Rosenkrantz and R.E. Stearns. Properties of deterministic top down grammars. *Information and Control* 17 (1970), 226-256.

437. D.J. Rosenkrantz and P.M. Lewis II. Deterministic left corner parsing. IEEE Conf. Record of the 11th Annual Symp. on *Switching and Automata Theory*, 1970, 139-152.

438. R.J. Ross, G. Hotz and D.B. Benson. A general Greibach normal form transformation. Report CS-78-048, Dept. of Computer Science, Washington State University, Pullman, Washington, 1978.

439. B.R. Rowland. Combining parsing and evaluation for attributed grammars. Ph.D. Thesis, University of Wisconsin, Madison, 1977.

440. J.M. Rushby. LR(k) sparse parsers and their optimization. Dept. of Computer Science, University of Newcastle-Upon-Tyne, England, Ph.D. Thesis, 1977.

441. J.M. Russel. An investigation of a FORTRAN grammar for use with a micro processor based LALR(1) translator writing system. Naval Postgraduate School, Monterey, California, March 1977.

442. H. Ruething and M. Schoenhold. Syntax-gesteuerte Uebersetzung mit Hilfe von LR(1)- Analysatoren. Diplomarbeit, Dept. of Computer Science, University of Dortmund, 1980.

443. P. Ruzicka. Local disambiguating transformation. In: *Mathematical Foundations of Computer Science*, J. Becvar (ed.), Lect. Notes in Comp. Sci. 32, Springer-Verlag, Berlin, 1975, 399-404.

444. P. Ruzicka. On the size of DeRemer's analyzer. *Kybernetika* (Prague) 11 (1975), 207-217.

445. G.M. Sacco. Un generatore di tavole di decisione ottimizzate per analizzatori sintattici SLR(1). Thesis, Univ. di Torino, 1976.

446. G.M. Sacco. Fast LR(k) analysis. Tech. Report CSD-TR 300, Computer Sciences Department, Purdue University, 1979.

447. R. Schauerte. Transformationen von LR(k)-Grammatiken. Diplomarbeit, Abteilung Informatik, Universitaet Goettingen, Goettingen, 1973.

448. R.M. Schell Jr. Methods for constructing parallel compilers for use in a multi-processor environment. Ph.D. Thesis, Department of Computer Science Report No.958, University of Illinois at Urbana-Champaign, February 1979.

449. V. Schneider. A system for designing fast programming language translators. Proc. *AFIPS Spring Joint Computer Conf.*, AFIPS Press, Arlington, Va., 1969, 777-792.

450. M. Schkolnick. The equivalence of reducing transition languages and deterministic languages. *Comm. ACM* 17 (1974), 517-519.

451. P. Schlichtiger. Kettengrammatiken: Ein Konzept zur Definition handhabbarer Grammatikklassen mit effizientem Analyseverhalten. Ph.D. Thesis, University of Kaiserslautern, 1980.

452. P. Schlichtiger. Partitioned chain grammars. In: *Automata, Languages and Programming,* J.W. de Bakker and J. van Leeuwen (eds.), Lect. Notes in Comp. Sci. 85, Springer-Verlag, Berlin, 1980, 555-568.

453. P. Schlichtiger. On the parsing of partitioned chain grammars. Interner Bericht Nr. 21/79, University of Kaiserslautern, 1979.

454. P. Schlichtiger. On how to construct efficiently parsable grammars. Interner Bericht Nr. 22/80, University of Kaiserslautern, 1980.

455. R.W. Sebesta and N.D. Jones. Parsers for indexed grammars. *Int. J. Comput. Inform. Sci.* 7 (1978), 345-359.

456. S. Sekimoto. A practical method of constructing LR(1) parsers and on the properties peculiar to LR(1) grammars. *Information Processing in Japan* 12 (1972), 100-105.

457. S. Sekimoto, K. Mukai and M. Sudo. A method of minimizing LR(k) parsers. *Systems, Computers, Controls* 4 (1973), 73-80.

458. S. Sekimoto, K. Mukai and M. Sudo. A reduction method of LR(k) parsers. *Trans. Inst. Electron. & Comm. Eng. Jpn.* (Japan), Vol.E61, No.6, June 1978, p.501.

459. S. Sekimoto. A characterization of look-ahead stateless DPDA's of a bottom-up type. *Trans. Inst. Electron. & Comm. Eng. Jpn.* Sect.E (Japan),

Vol.E63, No.6, 490-491, 1980.

460. S. Sekimoto. An extended result on the equivalence problem for LR-machines. *Trans. Inst. Electron. & Comm. Eng. Jpn.* Sect.E (Japan), Vol.E64, No.5, 374-374, 1981.

461. B. Shapiro. SLR(1) parser generator. National Technical Information Service, PB-249 127/2WC, February 1976.

462. A.S. Shumei. Accelerated syntactic analysis of symbolic programs. *Avtomat. i Telemekh.* 1976, No.5, 158-164 (Russian); translated as *Automat. Remote Control* 37 (1976), No.5, part 2, 783-788. [MR 56#10178, 1978].

463. R.K. Shyamasundar. Studies on parsing, syntax-directed translations and conditional grammars. Ph.D. Thesis, School of Automation, Indian Institute of Science, Bangalore, India, 1975.

464. R.K. Shyamasundar. Necessary and sufficient conditions for a power language to be deterministic. *Int. J. Computer Math.* 5 (1975), 133-142.

465. R.K. Shyamasundar. LR-deterministic grammars. *Elektronische Informations-verarbeitung und Kybernetik (EIK)* 14 (1978), 361-376.

466. B.A. Silverberg. Using a grammatical formalism as a programming language. Techn. Report CSRG-88, January 1978, University of Toronto.

467. S. Sippu. Error recovery in LR parsing (in Finnish). Master's Thesis. Internal Report C-1976-22. Dept. of Computer Science, University of Helsinki, 1976.

468. S. Sippu and E. Soisalon-Soininen. On defining error recovery in context-free parsing. In: *Automata, Languages and Programming,* A. Salomaa and M. Steinby (eds.), Lect. Notes in Comp. Sci. 52, Springer-Verlag, Berlin, 1977, 492-503.

469. S. Sippu and E. Soisalon-Soininen. Characterizations of the LL(k) property. In: *Automata, Languages and Programming,* J.W. de Bakker and J. van Leeuwen (eds.), Lect. Notes in Comp. Sci. 85, Springer-Verlag, Berlin, 1980, 596-608.

470. S. Sippu and E. Soisalon-Soininen. A scheme for LR(k) parsing with error recovery. Part I. LR(k) parsing. *Int. J. Computer Math.* 8 (1980), 27-42.

471. S. Sippu and E. Soisalon-Soininen. A scheme for LR(k) parsing with error recovery. Part II. Error recovery. *Int. J. Computer Math.* 8 (1980), 107-119.

472. S. Sippu and E. Soisalon-Soininen. A scheme for LR(k) parsing with error recovery. Part III. Error correction. *Int. J. Computer Math.* 8 (1980), 189-206.

473. S. Sippu and E. Soisalon-Soininen. On LALR(k) testing. In: *Automata, Languages and Programming,* S. Even and O. Kariv (eds.), Lect. Notes in Comp. Sci. 115, Springer-Verlag, Berlin, 1981, 208-217.

474. M. Snelling. General context-free parsing in time n square. In: *Int. Computing Symposium,* 1973, A. Gunther, B. Levrat and H. Lipps (eds.), American Elsevier Publ. Co., New York, 1974, 19-24.

475. Softech., Inc. An introduction to the features and uses of AED. Softech., Inc., Vol.6080, January 1975.

476. Softech., Inc. The compiler framework. Softech., Inc., Vol.7089, April 1976.

477. E. Soisalon-Soininen. Design of an automatic constructor of LR-parsers (in Finnish). Univ. of Helsinki, Dept. of Computer Science, Nr. 1976/27, January 1976.

478. E. Soisalon-Soininen and E. Ukkonen. A characterization of LL(k) languages. In: *Automata, Languages and Programming,* S. Michaelson and R. Milner (eds.), Edinburgh University Press, Edinburgh, 1976, 20-30.

479. E. Soisalon-Soininen. Elimination of single productions from LR parsers in conjunction with the use of default reductions. Conf. Record of the Fourth ACM Symp. on *Principles of Programming Languages,* 1977, 183-193.

480. E. Soisalon-Soininen. Characterization of LL(k) languages by restricted LR(k) grammars. Report A-1977-3, University of Helsinki.

481. E. Soisalon-Soininen and E. Ukkonen. A method for transforming grammars into LL(k) form. *Acta Informatica* 12 (1979), 339-369.

482. E. Soisalon-Soininen. On the space optimizing effect of eliminating single productions from LR parsers. *Acta Informatica* 14 (1980), 157-174.

483. E. Soisalon-Soininen. On comparing LL(k) and LR(k) grammars. *Math. Systems Theory* 13 (1980), 323-348.

484. E. Soisalon-Soininen. Inessential error entries and their use in LR parser optimization. *ACM Trans. Progr. Lang. Syst.* 4 (1982), 179-195.

485. D. Spector. Full LR(1) parser generation. *SIGPLAN Notices* 16, Nr.8, August 1981, 58-66. Also: Nr.11, November 1981, 2-2.

486. W.R. Strait. Formal model of translation with symbol table pointers. *ACM Comp. Sci. Conf.*, Washington, DC, 1975, p.40.

487. J. Suikkanen. Conflicts in the LALR(1) parsing automaton (in Finnish). Internal Report C-1979-5, November 1979.

488. P. Szmal. Global syntactic error correction for LR(1)-grammars (in Polish). *Podstawy Sterowania* 11 (1981), 201-218.

489. T.G. Szymanski. Generalized bottom-up parsing. Ph.D. Thesis, Cornell University, Ithaca, N.Y., 1973.

490. T.G. Szymanski. Concerning bounded-right-context grammars. *Theoret. Comput. Sci.* 3 (1976), 273-282.

491. T.G. Szymanski and J.H. Williams. Noncanonical extensions of bottom-up parsing techniques. *SIAM J. Computing* 5 (1976), 231-250.

492. K.-C. Tai. The recovery of parsing configurations for LR(1) parsers. Proc. 15th *Southeastern Regional ACM Conf., 1974, 154-160.*

493. K.-C. Tai. The recovery of parsing configurations for LR parsers. Tech. Rep. 77-06, Dept. of Computer Science, North Carolina State University, 1977.

494. K.-C. Tai. Syntactic error correction in programming languages. *IEEE Trans. on Software Eng.*, Vol. SE-4, 1978, 414-425.

495. K.-C. Tai. On the implementation of parsing tables. *SIGPLAN Notices* 14, Nr.1, January 1979, 100-101.

496. K.-C. Tai. Noncanonical SLR(1) grammars. *ACM Trans. Progr. Lang. Syst.* 1 (1979), 295-320.

497. K.-C. Tai. Predictors of context-free grammars. *SIAM J. Computing* 9 (1980), 653-664.

498. J. Tarhio. Parsing ambiguous grammars in the HLP system (in Finnish). Report C-1979-93, Dept. of Computer Science, University of Helsinki, 1979.

499. J. Tarhio. An LALR(1) syntax for extended Algol (in Finnish). Internal Report, 1980.

500. J. Tarhio. Attribute evaluation during LR parsing. Ph.Lic. Thesis, Dept. of Computer Science, University of Helsinki, 1982.

501. J. Tarhio. LR parsing of some ambiguous grammars. *Information Processing Letters* 14 (1982), 101-103.

502. G. Terrine. Construction automatique d'analyseurs syntaxiques ascendants deterministes a partir de CF grammaires eventuellement non de contexte borne. Doct. Thesis, Univ. of Grenoble, France, 1971.

503. G. Terrine. An algorithm generating the decision table of a deterministic bottom-up parser for a subset of context-free grammars. Proc. of the Third Annual ACM Symp. on *Theory of Computing,* 1971, 185-205.

504. G. Terrine. Coordinate grammars and parsers. *Computer Journal* 16 (1973), 232-244.

505. D.S. Terry. Ambiguity and LR parsing. Report 78-11-02, Dept. of Computer Science, University of Washington, Seattle, 1978.

506. D. Thimm. Kombination von sackgassenfreier Topdown- und Bottomup-Syntaxanalyse. *GI-5.Jahrestagung,* E.J. Muehlbacher (ed.), Lect. Notes in Comp. Sci. 34, Springer-Verlag, Berlin, 1975, 397-408.

507. D. Thimm. Effiziente Algorithmen zur Syntaxanalyse von Programmiersprachen. Ph.D. Thesis, Technische Universitaet Berlin, Institut fuer Technische Informatik, 1977.

508. D. Thimm. Kombinierte Topdown/Bottomup-Syntaxanalyse von LR(k) Grammatiken. *Elektronische Rechenanlagen* 20 (1978), 5.

509. D.H. Thompson. The design and implementation of an advanced LALR parse table construct. UT-CSRG-79 (1977), University of Toronto.

510. T. Tokuda. A new method for speeding up Knuth type LR(k) parsers. *Trans. Inst. Electron. & Comm. Eng. Jpn.* Sect.E (Japan), Vol.E63, No.10, p.792, 1980.

511. T. Tokuda. Eliminating unit reductions from LR(k) parsers using minimum contexts. *Acta Informatica* 15 (1981), 447-470.

512. P. Tori. Experiences on LR(k) parser generators. Thesis, Univ. of Genova, 1982, (in Italian).

513. C.J.M. Turnbull. Deterministic left to right parsing. CSRG-48, Univ. of Toronto, 1975.

514. C.J.M. Turnbull and E.S. Lee. Generalized deterministic left to right parsing. *Acta Informatica* 12 (1979), 187-207.

515. E. Ukkonen. Transformations to produce certain covering grammars. In: *Mathematical Foundations of Computer Science*, J. Winkowski (ed.), Lect.Notes in Comp. Sci. 64, Springer-Verlag, Berlin, 1978, 516-525.

516. E. Ukkonen. A modification of the LR(k) method for constructing compact bottom-up parsers. In: *Automata, Languages and Programming*, H.A. Maurer (ed.), Lect. Notes in Comp. Sci. 71, Springer-Verlag, Berlin, 1979, 646-658.

517. E. Ukkonen. A decision method for the equivalence of some non-real-time deterministic pushdown automata. Proc. 12th Annual ACM Symp. on *Theory of Computing*, 1980, 29-38.

518. E. Ukkonen and E. Soisalon-Soininen. LALR(k) testing is PSPACE-complete. Report C-1980-75, Dept. of Computer Science, University of Helsinki. Also: Proc. 13th ACM Symp. on *Theory of Computing*, 1981.

519. E. Ukkonen. Lower bounds on the size of deterministic parsers. Memorandum No. UCB/ERL M81/98, 1981, University of California, Berkeley.

520. E. Ukkonen. On size bounds for deterministic parsers. In: *Automata, Languages and Programming*, S. Even and O. Kariv (eds.), Lect. Notes in Comp. Sci. 115, Springer-Verlag, Berlin, 1981, 218-228.

521. J.D. Ullman. Applications of language theory to compiler design. In: *Currents in the Theory of Computing*. A.V. Aho (ed.), Prentice Hall, Englewood Cliffs, N.J., 1973, 173-218.

522. S. Ulukut. Implementierung eines LALR(1)-Analysators. Diplomarbeit, Universitaet Karlsruhe, Fakultaet fuer Informatik, December 1974.

523. M.K. Unklesbay. A one step version of Younger's algorithm for bounded context grammars. Report PB-197643, Ohio State University, 1970.

524. D. Varga. Problems of improving the efficiencies of parsing systems. *Computational Linguistics* 8 (1970), 71-93.

525. L.G. Valiant. Decision procedures for DPDA's. Ph.D. Thesis, University of Warwick, Warwick, England, 1973.

526. L.G. Valiant. General context-free recognition in less than cubic time. *J. Comput. System Sci.* 10 (1975), 308-315.

527. T. Venema. TRUST User's Guide. Technical manual, Dept. of Computer Science, University of British Columbia, 1976.

528. D.A. Walters. Deterministic context-sensitive languages. IEEE Tenth Annual Symp. on *Switching and Automata Theory,* 1969, 133-148.

529. D.A. Walters. Deterministic context-sensitive languages. *Information and Control* 17 (1970), 14-61.

530. D.A. Watt. LR-parsing of affix grammars. Dept. of Computer Science, University of Glasgow, Report No.7, 1974.

531. D.A. Watt. The parsing problem for affix grammars. *Acta Informatica* 8 (1977), 1-20.

532. D.A. Watt. Rule splitting and attribute directed parsing. In: *Semantics Directed Compiler Generation,* N.D. Jones (ed.), Lect. Notes in Comp. Sci. 94, Springer-Verlag, Berlin, 1980, 363-392.

533. M. Wegman. Parsing for structural editors. Conf. Record of 21st Annual Symp. on *Foundations of Computer Science,* 1980, 320-327.

534. L.M. Wegner. Analysis of two-level grammars. Ph.D. Thesis, Hochschulverlag, Stuttgart, 1977.

535. L.M. Wegner. On parsing two-level grammars. *Acta Informatica* 14 (1980), 175-193.

536. C.S. Wetherell. A correction to DeRemer's SLR(1) parser construction algorithm. Unpublished manuscript, Lawrence Livermore Laboratories, Livermore.

537. C.S. Wetherell and A. Shannon. LR automatic parser generator and LR(1) parser. *IEEE Trans. Softw. Eng.* SE-7 (1981), 247-278.

538. C.S. Wetherell. Problems with the ADA reference grammar. *SIGPLAN Notices* 16, Nr.9, September 1981, 90-104.

539. R.M. Wharton. Resolution of ambiguity in parsing. *Acta Informatica* 6 (1976), 387-395.

540. P. White. On error recovery of LR parsers. Computing Laboratory, University of Newcastle-Upon-Tyne, MRM, 1974.

541. R. Wilhelm. LL- and LR-attributed grammars. In: *Programmiersprachen und Programmentwicklung,* H. Woessner (ed.), GI-7.Fachtagung, Informatik Fachberichte 53, Springer-Verlag, Berlin, 1982, 151-164.

542. J.H. Williams. Bounded context parsable grammars. Technical Report No.58, Computer Science Department, Univ. of Wisconsin, Madison, March 1969.

543. J.H. Williams. Bounded context parsable grammars and parsers. *Information and Control* 28 (1975), 314-334.

544. D.S. Wise. Domolki's algorithm applied to generalized overlap resolvable grammars. Proc. of the Third Annual ACM Symp. on *Theory of Computing,* 1971, 171-184.

545. D.S. Wise. Generalized overlap resolvable grammars, languages, and parsers. Report #1174, Mathematics Research Center, University of Wisconsin, January 1972.

546. D.S. Wise. Generalized overlap resolvable grammars and parsers. *J. Comput. System Sci.* 6 (1972), 538-572.

547. J. Witaszek. The LR(k) parser. In: *Mathematical Foundations of Computer Science,* P. Dembinski (ed.), Lect. Notes in Comp. Sci. 88, Springer-Verlag, Berlin, 1980, 686-697.

548. J. Witaszek. Construction and optimization of LR(k) parsers (in Polish). Dissertation, IMM, Warsaw, 1979.

549. D. Wood. Bibliography 23. Formal Language Theory and Automata Theory. *Computing Reviews* 11 (1970), Nr.7, 417-430.

550. D. Wood. A bibliography of top-down parsing. *SIGPLAN Notices* 13, Nr.2, February 1978, 71-76.

551. R.A. Woods. A PL360-based compiler generating system (SLR). Master's Thesis, Naval Postgraduate School, Monterey, California, 1972, AD-757 260.

552. D.A. Workman. SR(s,k) parsers: A class of shift-reduce bounded context parsers. *J. Comput. System Sci.* 22 (1981), 178-197.

553. D. Wotschke. The Boolean closures of the deterministic and nondeterministic context-free languages. In: *GI-3.Jahrestagung,* W. Brauer (ed.), Lect. Notes in Comp. Sci. 1, Springer-Verlag, Berlin, 1973, 113-121.

554. P. Wynn. Error recovery in SLR parsers. Ph.D. Thesis, University of Newcastle-Upon-Tyne, 1973.

555. O. Yamada, S. Noguchi and J. Oizumi. MR(m,n) grammar and its syntactic analysis. *Systems, Computers, Controls* 3 (1972), No.2, 57-65.

556. S. Yamasaki and T. Tonomura. On a bottom-up least error correction algorithm for context-free languages (in Japanese). *Inf. Process. Soc. Jpn.* 18 (1977), No.8, 781-788.

557. A. Yehudai. On the complexity of grammar and language problems. Ph.D. Thesis, University of California, Berkeley, 1977.

558. A. Yehudai. A hierarchy of real-time strict deterministic languages and their equivalence. *J. Comput. System Sci.* 24 (1982), 91-100.

559. D.H. Younger. Recognition and parsing of context-free languages in time n-cubic. *Information and Control* 10 (1967), 189-208.

560. S.F. Zeigler. Smaller faster table driven parser. Unpublished manuscript, Madison Academic Computing Centre, University of Wisconsin, Madison, 1977.

561. V.S. Zonis and A.S. Shumei. Optimization of a syntactic analyzer that is constructed according to the method of LR(k) grammars (Russian). *Program-mirovanie* 1976, No.2, 3-9, 95. [MR 55#11737, 1978].

4. PRECEDENCE PARSING: A BIBLIOGRAPHY

SURVEY OF THE LITERATURE

4.1. General and History

This bibliography contains references to papers in which precedence relations are used. Other recently compiled bibliographies on parsing deal with:

- top-down parsing (see Section 2 of this Monograph and Wood[244])

- LR-grammars and parsing (see Section 3 of this Monograph and Burgess and James[39])

- error handling (Ciesinger[41])

- translator writing tools (Meijer and Nijholt[168])

In Floyd[75] (1963) operator precedence relations and operator precedence grammars were introduced. In Wirth and Weber[238] (1966) the Wirth-Weber precedence relations and the simple precedence grammars are defined. Independently, Pair[179] has introduced simple precedence grammars in 1964. Precedence relations have been used in parsing and compiler construction before the appearance of the formal definitions in these two papers. Although a few papers are mentioned, this bibliography does not fully cover such publications. In Bauer[32] some notes on early research in parsing can be found. In that paper it is mentioned that the origins of precedence parsing can be traced back to at least 1956.

Apart from these papers the bibliography contains papers on the use of precedence relations in formal language theory (parsing, algebraic properties, graph grammars, grammatical inference, grammar forms, EOL-systems) and in compiler construction. Papers on Domolki's syntax analysis algorithm are also included in this bibliography.

4.2. Properties of Grammars and Languages

In Aho and Ullman[2] precedence relations have been used in order to give a formal proof of the theorem that every deterministic language can be generated with an LR(1) grammar. Properties of precedence grammars and languages were first investigated by Fischer[74]. Graham[87] has extensively studied the relationships between precedence grammars and Floyd's bounded context grammars. Among others it is shown which class of precedence grammars is able to generate exactly the deterministic languages. Gray and Harrison[92] consider combinations of precedence and LR parsing techniques and they consider transformations from LR grammars to grammars for which such combined parsing techniques can be used. Yehudai[246] discusses some aspects of the definition of simple precedence grammars. A recent discussion on the role of precedence relations in the theory of parsing can be found in Nijholt[174].

In Floyd's scheme the relations are defined between the terminal symbols. Moreover, the grammar under consideration is supposed to be in operator form. That is, no two adjacent nonterminal symbols are allowed in the righthand sides of the grammar rules. A drawback of Floyd's scheme is that the corresponding precedence parsing algorithm can accept a superset of the language of the grammar. In Ruzicka[199] an algorithm is presented which can be used to decide whether the parsing algorithm accepts exactly the language of the underlying grammar. Another approach to this problem is followed by Henderson and Levy[104] and Levy[148]. They modify the precedence relations in an attempt to overcome this discrepancy. Unfortunately their attempts are not quite satisfactory (cf. Williams[232-234]).

Wirth and Weber generalize Floyd's scheme by defining precedence relations on the entire vocabulary. Moreover, the restriction to operator form is relaxed. In this way the simple precedence grammars are obtained. Other authors have further generalized this scheme and have defined combinations with bounded context techniques. In this way extended precedence, weak precedence, soft precedence, strong precedence, left local precedence, strict precedence, total precedence, parallel total precedence, right precedence, mixed strategy precedence, extended operator precedence and weak operator precedence grammars have been defined. This list is not complete. Among them the weak precedence grammars, introduced by Ichbiah and Morse[118], and the mixed strategy precedence grammars, introduced by McKeeman et al[164], have turned out to be practically useful. Colmerauer[48] and Gray and Harrison[93] present general theories of precedence analysis.

4.3. Precedence Relations and Functions

The precedence relations can be stored in a matrix, the so-called precedence matrix. This matrix is then used in the implementation of the parsing method. Research in the area of precedence parsing has centered on the possibility to reduce the storage requirements of this matrix, without affecting the parsing algorithm, and on methods to transform non-precedence grammars to precedence grammars. Reducing the storage requirements has been done by compressing the precedence matrix to linear precedence functions. If n is the size of the vocabulary of the grammar, then n x n is the size of the matrix of precedence relations. However, for the precedence functions it is only necessary to store 2n entries.

Algorithms to compute the precedence relations have been given by Floyd[75], Martin[156], Wirth and Weber[238] and Hunt, Szymanski and Ullman[116]. In the latter paper it is shown that this computation can be done in O(nxn) steps, where n is the size of the grammar. Computation of linear precedence functions has been considered by Floyd[75], Wirth and Weber[238], Wirth[239], Aho and Ullman[3], Bell[34,35], Martin[157], Bertsch[36] and Duong-Kien et al[65]. See Aoe et al[12], Er[69] and Hunt, Szymanski and Ullman[116] for more recent results. In the latter paper it is shown that this computation can be done in O(n) steps. Unfortunately, not for all precedence grammars there exist precedence functions. Moreover, the reduction of storage requirements can cause weaker error detection and recovery properties of the parser.

Algorithms to transform grammars to precedence grammars can be found in Fischer[74], Haynes[102], Lim[149], Learner and Lim[143], McAfee and Presser [161], Presser[185] and Presser and Melkanoff[186].

4.4. Parsing and Error-Handling

Precedence relations have played an important role in the theory and practise of building parsers, compilers and compiler writing systems. Cf. Hoare[111], McClure[162] and Aho and Ullman[2]. Compilers have been constructed with a parsing module based on precedence relations. Cf. Bauer, Becker and Graham[33] for an ALGOL compiler, Dewar and McCann[59] for a SNOBOL compiler and Natt and Simon[174] for an EULER compiler. Lindsey and Turner[150,151] and Meertens and van Vliet[167] have used precedence methods in the parsing and error recovery for ALGOL 68. The original version of the XPL compiler writing system (McKeeman, Horning and Wortman[165]) was based on precedence analysis (later replaced by an algorithm utilizing LR(k) techniques). LeCarme and Bochmann[144], Ichbiah and Morse[118], White and Presser[231] (the UCSB translator writing system) and Zimmer[250] describe other wellknown examples of parser generating systems based on precedence relations. See also Cook[49] and Schwenkel[203,204].

Precedence parsers for various programming languages have been compared empirically with other types of parsers. Both time and space requirements for precedence parsers are, sometimes considerably, larger than for SLR(1) and LALR(1) parsers (Horning and LaLonde[114]). However, good comparisons are difficult since, among others, the generality of the parsing method, the possibility to work for "natural" programming language grammars, and error detection and recovery possibilities should be taken into account. Nevertheless, the existing comparisons are biased in favor of non-precedence methods. Feldman and Gries[71] remark that a grammar for an average programming language has to be manipulated considerably before it is a precedence grammar. This can be contrasted with what has been called DeRemer's Thesis: "If a designer sets out to design an unambiguous CF grammar to specify the *structural properties* of a language, his result will be an LR(k) grammar." DeRemer's Thesis has been confirmed, and in fact refined to LALR(1) grammars, in various papers which are included in the LR-Bibliography.

After 1972 LR(1) and LL(1) parsing methods have become the main tools for building parsers and the parser generating part of translator writing systems (cf. Meijer and Nijholt[168]). However, there exist some interesting exceptions.

Precedence relations can be defined for various classes of grammars which are more general than the context-free grammars. They have been used for OL systems (Hladky[110]), graph grammars (Franck[77] and Kaul[131]) and context-sensitive and general phrase structure grammars (Khabbaz[132], Babinov[25] and Haskell [100]). In the latter paper a transformation from general phrase structure grammars to precedence form is given. Moreover, precence relations appear in the definitions of subclasses of the indexed grammars (cf. Ordjan and Dzulakjan[178]) and in the area of parallel parsing methods (Fischer[72] and Pronina[191]).

Error-correcting techniques for simple precedence grammars have been given by Wirth[236], Leinius[146] and Rhodes[193] (see also Graham and Rhodes[89]). Some of the earlier methods are language-dependent. Hence, automatic generation of error-correcting parsers is not always possible with these methods. Certain parsing methods can announce errors as soon as the part of the input which has been seen thus far does no longer form a prefix of a sentence in the language. None of the methods in the above mentioned papers has this *Correct Prefix Property*. In Geller, Graham and Harrison[82] and in Moll[171] classes of grammars are defined for which parsers can have this property. Recently, various reports and theses have been published at West-German universities in which error correcting methods for precedence parsers are introduced (cf., among others, Buechler[38], Hauger[101], Gonser[85] and Richter[194]). Error recovery for precedence parsers has also been considered by Ripley[196].

REFERENCES

1. A.V. Aho, P.J. Denning and J.D. Ullman. Weak and mixed strategy precedence parsing. *J. Assoc. Comput. Mach.* 19 (1972), 225-243.

2. A.V. Aho and J.D. Ullman. *The Theory of Parsing, Translation, and Compiling.* Vols. 1 and 2. Prentice Hall, Englewood Cliffs, N.J., 1972 and 1973.

3. A.V. Aho and J.D. Ullman. Linear precedence functions for weak precedence grammars. *Int. J. Computer Math.* 3 (1972), 149-155.

4. A.V. Aho and J.D. Ullman. Error detection in precedence parsers. *Math. Systems Theory* 7 (1972), 97-113.

5. A.V. Aho and J.D. Ullman. *Principles of Compiler Design.* Addison-Wesley, Reading, Mass., 1977.

6. H. Alblas. Illegale strings in een operator precedentie taal. ALG. VGP 033, Vakgroep Informatica, Twente University of Technology, Manuscript, 1970.

7. J. Aoe, Y. Yamamoto, N. Harada and R. Shimada. A construction of weak precedence functions. *Trans. Inst. Electron. & Comm. Eng. Jpn.* (Japan), Vol.E60, No.1, Jan. 1977, 66-67.

8. J. Aoe, Y. Yamamoto and R. Shimada. Simulation and its evaluation for weak precedence parsers. *Trans. Inst. Electron. & Comm. Eng. Jpn.* (Japan) Vol.E60, No.10, Oct. 1977, p.605.

9. J.Aoe, Y. Yamamoto and R. Shimada. On grammar-modification for right precedence relation. *Trans. Inst. Electron. & Comm. Eng. Jpn.* (Japan) Vol.E60, No.10, Oct. 1977, p.606.

10. J. Aoe, Y. Yamamoto, N. Harada and R. Shimada. The construction of weak precedence parsers by parsing tables (in Japanese). *Inf. Process. Soc. Jpn.* 18 (1977), No.5, 438-444.

11. J. Aoe, Y. Yamamoto and R. Shimada. Practical method for reducing precedence parsers. *Trans. Inst. Electron. & Comm. Eng. Jpn.* (Japan) Vol.E61, No.6, June 1978, p.499.

12. J. Aoe, Y. Yamamoto and R. Shimada. Practical method for reducing precedence parsers. *Systems, Computers, Controls* 9 (1978), 54-62 (1980).

13. J. Aoe, Y. Yamamoto and R. Shimada. Supplement to practical method for reducing precedence parsers. *Trans. Inst. Electron. & Comm. Eng. Jpn.* Sect. E (Japan), Vol.E62, No.9, 639-639, 1979.

14. J. Aoe, Y. Yamamoto and R. Shimada. Error recovery and simulations of reduced precedence parsers. *Trans. Inst. Electron. & Comm. Eng. Jpn.* Sect. E (Japan), Vol.E62, No.10, 731-731, 1979.

15. J. Aoe, Y. Yamamoto and R. Shimada. A technique for generating optimal parsers for precedence grammars. *Bull. Fac. Eng. Tokushima Univ.*, Vol.15 (1978), 39-49.

16. B.W. Arden, B.A. Galler and R.M. Graham. *Michigan Algorithmic Decoder.* University of Michigan Press, Ann Arbor, Mich., 1966.

17. K. Asai. Precedence grammars with precedence functions. *Information Processing in Japan* 11 (1971), 185-194.

18. K. Asai. On existence of precedence functions of precedence grammars (in Japanese). *Joho-Shori* 13 (1972), 218-224.

19. K. Asai. On existence of precedence functions of precedence grammars. *Information Processing in Japan* 12 (1972), 113-118.

20. R.E. Asratyan. A generalization of the precedence method. *Program. Comput. Software* 5 (1979), 318-322.

21. A.V. Babicev. Automata that recognize languages generated by precedence grammars (in Russian). *Programmirovanie* 1978, No. 6, 20-25.

22. A.V. Babicev, V.A. Pronina and E.A. Trahtengerc. The reduction of generating grammars to a form that contains precedence functions (in Russian). *Programmirovanie* 1977, No. 3, 43-53.

23. J.P. Babinov. Context grammars of precedence (in Russian). In: *Obrabotha Simvol'noy Info. (Proc. Symbol. Info.)*, Comp. CTR USSR Acad.Sci., Moscow, No.2, 1975, 90-97.

24. J.P. Babinov. Two classes of non contractive (shortened) precedence grammars (Russian). *Z. Vycisl. Mat. i Mat. Fiz* 16 (1976), No.4, 1027-1037, 1086. [MR 55#1830, 1978]. English translation in: *USSR Comput. Math. and Math. Phys.* (GB).

25. J.P. Babinov. Class of generalized context-sensitive precedence languages. *Program. Comput. Software* 5 (1979), 117-126.

26. F. Bacelli and T. Fleuri. Analyse syntaxique en environnement parallele. Rapports de Recherche No.49, INRIA (Inst. National de Recherche en Informatique et en Automatique), Le Chesnay, January 1981.

27. F. Bacelli and T. Fleuri. On parsing arithmetic expressions in a multi-processing environment. *Acta Informatica* 17 (1982), 287-310.

28. S. Backes. Automatische Erzeugung von Syntax-Analyse-Programmen. *Elektronische Rechenanlagen* 12 (1970), 80-86.

29. K.R. Barnes. Exploratory steps towards a grammatical manipulation package (GRAMPA). Master's Dissertation, McMaster University, 1972.

30. W.A. Barrett and J.D. Couch. *Compiler Construction: Theory and Practice.* Science Research Associates, Inc., 1979.

31. F.L. Bauer and K. Samelson. The cellar principle for formula translation. Proc. *ICIP* , Paris, 1959, p. 154.

32. F.L. Bauer. Historical remarks on compiler construction. In: *Compiler Construction: An Advanced Course.* F.L. Bauer and J. Eickel (eds.), Lect. Notes in Comp. Sci. 21, Springer-Verlag, Berlin, 1974, 603-621.

33. H. Bauer, S. Becker and S.L. Graham. ALGOL W implementation. Report CS98, Computer Science Department, Stanford University, Stanford, California, 1968.

34. J.R. Bell. A new method for determining linear precedence functions for precedence grammars. *Comm. ACM* 12 (1969), 316-333.

35. J.R. Bell. A compression method for compiler precedence tables. Booklet 2, 359-362. *IFIP Congress 74.* Stockholm, Sweden.

36. E. Bertsch. The storage requirement in precedence parsing. *Comm. ACM* 20 (1977), 192-194.

37. B.P. Buckles, B.C. Hodges and P. Hsia. A survey of compiler development aids. NASA TM X-3490, George C. Marshall Space Flight Center, Alabama, 1977.

38.   A. Buechler. Entwicklung eines neuen Fehlerbehandlungsalgorithmus fuer einfache Praezedenzesprachen. Inst. fuer Informatik, Technische Universitaet Muenchen, Diplomarbeit, 1977.

39.   C. Burgess and L. James. An indexed bibliography for LR grammars and parsers. *SIGPLAN Notices* 16, Nr.8, August 1981, 14-26.

40.   E.A. Calderon. A multilingual compiler for stack-oriented computers. Report, University of Pennsylvania, Moore School of Electrical Engineering, Philadelphia, 1969.

41.   J. Ciesinger. A bibliography of error-handling. *SIGPLAN Notices* 14, Nr.1, January 1979, 16-26.

42.   J. Cohen. Experience with a conversational parser generating system. *Software-Practice and Experience* 5 (1975), 169-180.

43.   J. Cohen and R. Sitver. A case study in program transformation: translation into Polish. *IEEE Trans. Softw. Eng.* 6 (1979), 575-586.

44.   J. Cohen and A. Rubin. BNF of BNF in precedence form: its use in constructing precedence tables. *RAIRO, Chiffres,* B-1, 1972.

45.   A. Colmerauer. Relations de precedence dans une grammaire "context free". Actes du Cinquieme Congres de l'AFIRO, 1966, Assoc. Francaise Informat. Recherches Operationnelles, Paris, 1966, 139-144.

46.   A. Colmerauer. Notions d'operateurs dans une grammaire "context-free". *R.I.R.O. (Revue Francaise d'Informatique et de Recherche Operationelle)* 1 (1967), 55-97.

47.   A. Colmerauer. Precedence, Analyse Syntaxique et Langages de Programmation. Ph.D. Thesis, University of Grenoble, 1967.

48.   A. Colmerauer. Total precedence relations. *J. Assoc. Comput. Mach.* 17 (1970), 14-30.

49.   R.P. Cook. A tabular compilation system for augmented precedence parsing. Proc. of the Eight *Texas Conf. on Computing Systems,* Southern Methodist University, Dallas, Texas, 1979, 4A/15-4A/20.

50.   S. Crespi-Reghizzi. Error-detecting precedence functions. In: Proc. of the Second *Hawaii Int. Conf. on System Science,* Honolulu, 1969, 669-702.

51. S. Crespi-Reghizzi and P. Della Vigna. Minimal solutions of Boolean matrix equation. Report Nr.69-23, Istituto di Elettrotechnica ed Elettronica del Politecnico di Milano, September 1969.

52. S. Crespi-Reghizzi. The mechanical acquisition of precedence grammars. Ph.D. Thesis, University of California, Los Angeles, 1970.

53. S. Crespi-Reghizzi, D. Mandrioli and D.F. Martin. Algebraic properties of operator precedence languages. *Information and Control* 37 (1978), 115-133.

54. S. Crespi-Reghizzi, G. Guida and D. Mandrioli. Operator precedence grammars and the non-counting property. *SIAM J. Computing* 10 (1981), 174-191.

55. A.J. Demers. Skeletal LR parsing. IEEE Conf. Record of 15th Annual Symp. on *Switching and Automata Theory*, 185-198, 1974.

56. F.L. DeRemer. Practical translators for LR(k) languages. Ph.D. Thesis, MIT, Cambridge, Mass., September, 1969.

57. P. Deussen. One abstract accepting algorithm for all kinds of parsers. In: *Automata, Languages and Programming*, H.A. Maurer (ed.), Lect. Notes in Comp. Sci. 71, Springer-Verlag, Berlin, 1979,, 203-217.

58. P. Deussen. A unified approach to the generation and acceptance of formal languages. *Acta Informatica* 9 (1978), 377-390.

59. R.B.K. Dewar and A.P. McCann. Macro Spitbol- a SNOBOL 4 compiler. *Software-Practice and Experience* 7 (1977), 95-113.

60. E.-W. Dieterich. Parsing and syntactic error recovery for context-free grammars by means of coarse structures. In: *Automata, Languages and Programming*, A. Salomaa and M. Steinby (eds.), Lect. Notes in Comp. Sci. 52, Springer-Verlag, Berlin, 1977, 180-192.

61. B. Domolki. An algorithm for syntactic analysis. *Computational Linguistics* (Hungarian journal) 3 (1964), 29-46.

62. B. Domolki. Algorithm for the recognition of sequences of symbols. *Z. Vychisl. Mat. i Mat. Fiz.* 5 (1965), No.1, 77-97. English translation in: *USSR Comput. Math. and Math. Phys.* 5, Pergamon Press, 1967, 101-130.

63. B. Domolki. A universal compiler system based on production rules. *BIT (Nordisk Tidskrift for Informationsbehandling)* 8 (1968), 262-275.

64. C. Duong-Kien. Eine Implementierung der totalen und einfachen Praezedenz-verfahren. Preparatory Th. PU-S3, Dept. of Computer Science, Technische Universitaet Darmstadt, August 1974.

65. C. Duong-Kien, H.-J. Hoffmann and D. Muth. An improvement to Martin's algorithm for computation of linear precedence functions. *Comm. ACM* 19 (1976), 576-577.

66. J. Earley. Ambiguity and precedence in syntax description. *Acta Informatica* 4 (1975), 183-192.

67. N. El Djabri. LR(1) parsers for precedence grammars. Report, Comp. Sci. Lab., Dept. of Electr. Eng., Princeton University, 1973.

68. N. El Djabri. Extending the LR parsing technique to some non-LR grammars. TR-121, Princeton University, 1973.

69. M.C. Er. A note on computing precedence functions. *Computer Journal* 25 (1982), 397-398.

70. W.M. Evangelist. An extension of the operator precedence parsing technique. M.S. Thesis, Dept. of Computer Sci., Northwestern University, Evanston, Il, 1978.

71. J. Feldman and D. Gries. Translator writing systems. *Comm. ACM* 11 (1968), 77-113.

72. C.N. Fischer. Parsing context-free languages in parallel environments. Ph.D. Thesis, Tech. Rep. 75-237, Dept. of Computer Science, Cornell University, 1975.

73. C.N. Fischer. On parsing and compiling arithmetic expressions in parallel computational environments. Report TR243, Computer Sciences Department, University of Wisconsin, Madison, March 1975.

74. M.J. Fischer. Some properties of precedence languages. Proc. ACM Symp. on *Theory of Computing*, 1969, 181-190.

75. R.W. Floyd. Syntactic analysis and operator precedence. *J. Assoc. Comput. Mach.* 10 (1963), 316-333.

76. R.W. Floyd. The syntax of programming languages - a survey. *IEEE Trans. on Electr. Computers*, Vol.EC-13, 1964, 346-353.

77. R. Franck. PLAN2D - Syntactic analysis of precedence graph grammars. In: 3rd ACM Symposium on *Principles of Programming Languages,* 1976, 134-139.

78. R. Franck. Precedence graph grammars: Theoretical results and documentation of an implementation. Forschungsbericht FB 20, TU Berlin, Nr. 77-10, 1977.

79. P.H. Frost. Bottom-up syntax analysis by Domolki's algorithm. Unpublished paper, Basser Computing Department, University of Sydney, Australia, 1966.

80. P.H. Frost and D.J. Langridge. A FORTRAN interpreter for use with on-line displays. Proc. 3rd Australian Computer Conference, 1966, 345-347.

81. B. Galler and A.J. Perlis. A proposal for definitions in ALGOL. *Comm. ACM* 10 (1967), 204-219.

82. M.M. Geller, S.L. Graham and M.A. Harrison. Production prefix parsing. In: *Automata, Languages and Programming,* J. Loeckx (ed.), Lect. Notes in Comp. Sci. 14, Springer-Verlag, Berlin, 1974, 232-241.

83. S. Ginsburg and D. Wood. Precedence relations on grammar forms. *Acta Informatica* 11 (1978), 79-88.

84. L.I. Goncharova. Precedence analysis and context conditions. *Zh. Vychisl. Mat. i Mat. Fiz.* (USSR) 15 (1975), No.3, 713-727. Translated in: *USSR Comput. Math. and Math. Phys.* (GB).

85. P. Gonser. Behandlung syntaktischer Fehler unter Verwendung kurzer fehlereinschliessender Intervalle (Treatment of syntax errors using short error-containing intervals). Ph. D. Thesis, Techn. University of Munich, Spring 1982.

86. S.L. Graham. Extended precedence languages, bounded right context languages and deterministic languages. IEEE Conf. Record of 11th Annual Symposium on *Switching and Automata Theory,* 1970, 175-180.

87. S.L. Graham. Precedence languages and bounded right context languages. Ph. D. Thesis, Dept. of Comput. Sci., Stanford University, California, 1971.

88. S.L. Graham and S.P. Rhodes. Practical syntactic error recovery in compilers. Conf. Record of ACM Symposium on *Principles of Programming Languages,* 1973, 52-58.

89. S.L. Graham and S.P. Rhodes. Practical syntactic error recovery. *Comm. ACM* 18 (1975), 639-650.

90. J.N. Gray. Precedence parsers for programming languages. Ph. D. Thesis , University of California at Berkeley, 1969.

91. J.N. Gray and M.A. Harrison. single pass precedence analysis. IEEE Conf. Record of 10th Annual Symp. on *Switching and Automata Theory* 1969, 106-117.

92. J.N. Gray and M.A. Harrison. On the covering and reduction problems for context-free grammars. *J. Assoc. Comput. Mach.* 19 (1972), 385-395.

93. J.N. Gray and M.A. Harrison. Canonical precedence schemes. *J. Assoc. Comput. Mach.* 20 (1973), 214-234.

94. D. Gries. M. Paul and H.R. Wiehle. Some techniques used in the ALCOR-ILLINOIS 7090. *Comm. ACM* 8 (1965), 496-500.

95. D. Gries. Use of transition matrices in compiling. *Comm. ACM* 11 (1968), 26-34.

96. D. Gries. *Compiler Construction for Digital Computers*. Wiley, New York, 1971.

97. F. Hadlock. Derived grammars with applications to syntactic analysis. Proc. 3rd Annual Princeton Conf. on *Information Sciences and Systems,* 1969, 413-416.

98. Hao Ke-Gang. The GP-grammar and the matching precedence parsing algorithm (in Chinese). *Chin. J. Comput.* 4 (1981), 21-27.

99. M.A. Harrison. On covers and precedence analysis. In: *GI-3.Jahrestagung,* W. Brauer (ed.), Lect. Notes in Comp. Sci. 1, Springer-Verlag, Berlin, 1973, 2-17.

100. R. Haskell. Symmetrical precedence relations on general phrase structure grammars. *Computer Journal* 17 (1974), 234-241. See also: 18 (1975), p.191.

101. F. Hauger. Ein neues Verfahren zur Behandlung von syntaktischen Fehlern bei einfachen Praezedenzsprachen. Inst. fuer Informatik, Technische Universitaet Muenchen, Diplomarbeit, 1978.

102. H.R. Haynes. Extended simple precedence syntactical analysis. Ph. D. Thesis, Texas, 1969.

103. S. Heilbrunner. Using item grammars to prove LR(k) theorems. Bericht Nr. 7701, Fachbereich Informatik, Hochschule der Bundeswehr Muenchen, 1977.

104. D.S. Henderson and M.R. Levy. An extended operator precedence parsing algorithm. *Computer Journal* 19 (1976), 229-233.

105. J.B. Hext and P.S. Roberts. Syntax analysis by Domolki's algorithm. *Computer Journal* 13 (1970), 263-271.

106. J.B. Hext. Syntax analysis by Domolki's algorithm. Basser Computing Dept., Techn. Rep. No. 52, University of Sydney, 1969.

107. M. Hladky. Precedence relations and their connection with unambiguity of context-free grammars. *Kybernetika* (Prague) 8 (1972), 1-11.

108. M. Hladky. Generalized simple precedence grammars. *Sp. Vysoke.* Uceni Tech. v. Brne, 1974, No.1-4, 237-243.

109. M. Hladky. Simple precedence OL-systems and production ambiguity. *Kniznice Odborn. Ved. Spisu Vysoke,* Uceni Tech. v. Brne A 12 (1976), 107-113 (1978).

110. M. Hladky. Precedence oriented parsing and OL-systems. *Libyan J. Sci.* 8 (1978), 63-70.

111. C.A.R. Hoare. Hints on programming language design. Stanford CS Report, 1973.

112. F.R.A. Hopgood. *Compiling Techniques.* Computer Monographs No.8, American Elsevier, New York, 1969.

113. J.J. Horning. Empirical comparison of LR(k) and precedence parsers. Memorandum, Computer Syst. Res. Gr., University of Toronto, August 1970.

114. J.J. Horning and W.R. LaLonde. Empirical comparison of LR(k) and precedence parsers. Tech. Rep. CSRG-1, Computer Syst. Res. Gr., University of Toronto, September 1970. Also in: *SIGPLAN Notices* 5, Nr.11, November 1970, 10-24.

115. H.B. Hunt III, T.G. Szymanski and J.D. Ullman. Operations on sparse relations and efficient algorithms for grammar problems. In: 15th IEEE Symp. on *Switching and Automata Theory,* 1974, 127-132.

116. H.B. Hunt III, T.G. Szymanski and J.D. Ullman. Operations on sparse relations. *Comm. ACM* 20 (1977), 171-176.

117. H.B. Hunt III and D.J. Rosenkrantz. Efficient algorithms for structural similarity of grammars. Conf. Record of Seventh ACM Symp. on *Principles of Programming Languages*, 1980, 213-219.

118. J.D. Ichbiah and S.P. Morse. A technique for generating almost optimal Floyd-Evans productions for precedence grammars. *Comm. ACM* 13 (1970), 501-508.

119. S. Iimori and S. Huzino. List processing for finding Wirth-Weber type precedence relations between symbols. *Mem. Fac. Sci. Kyushu Univ.*, Ser. A25 (1971), 152-166.

120. K. Inoue. Right precedence grammars (in Japanese). *Joho-Shori* 11 (1970), Nr.8.

121. K. Inoue. Right precedence grammars. *Information Processing in Japan* 11 (1971), 24-29.

122. K. Inoue. Right precedence grammars and their inclusion relations to other grammars. *Information Processing in Japan* 13 (1973), 49-53.

123. W. Issel. Ueber einige Probleme der Umformung der Syntax von ALGOL 60 in eine Operator-Praeferenz-Grammatik und der syntaktische Analyse von ALGOL 60 mit dieser Grammatik. *Elektronische Informationsverarbeitung und Informatik (EIK)* 8 (1972), 211-223.

124. C.B. Johns. The generation of error recovering simple precedence parsers. Master's Dissertation, Dept. of Applied Math., McMaster University, Hamilton, Ontario, July 1974.

125. K. Kaijiri, S. Uchinami and Y. Tezuka. Extended precedence parsing method and its error detection. *Tech. Rep. Osaka Univ.* 26 (1976), No.1276-1307, 13-34.

126. S. Kaijiri and S. Uchinami. On the realization methods of the precedence functions with error detecting capabilities. *Trans. Inst. Electron. & Comm. Eng. Jpn.* (Japan), Vol.E59, No.11, Nov. 1976, p.51.

127. K. Kaijiri, T. Seno, S. Uchinami and Y. Tezuka. The construction methods of weak precedence functions by postponement of error detection. *Trans. Inst. Electron. & Comm. Eng. Jpn.* (Japan), Vol.E59, No.11, Nov. 1976, p.50-51.

128. K. Kaijiri, S. Uchinami and Y. Tezuka. Extended weak precedence functions (in Japanese). *Inf. Process. Soc. Jpn.* 18 (1977), No.6, 542-549.

129. Z. Kasa. On Domolki's syntax analyzer implementation (in Roumanian). *Stud. Univ. Babes-Bolyai,* Math.26, No.1, 1981, 15-23.

130. M. Kaul. Syntax analysis of precedence graph-grammars. 2nd Int. Workshop on *Graph Grammars and their Application to Computer Science,* 1982.

131. M. Kaul. Linear precedence parsing for a new class of graph grammars. Proc. of the 7th Conf. on *Graphtheoretic Concepts in Computer Science,* J.R. Muehlbacher (ed.), Carl Hanser Verlag, Muenchen, Wien, 1982, 33-43.

132. N.A. Khabbaz. Multipass precedence analysis. *Acta Informatica* 4 (1974), 77-85.

133. J. Kral. Almost top-down analysis for generalized LR(k) grammars. In: *Methods of Algorithmic Language Implementation.* A. Ershov and C.H.A. Koster (eds.), Lect. Notes in Comp. Sci. 47, Springer-Verlag, Berlin, 1977, 149-172.

134. M. Kretinsky. Semi-top-down syntax analysis of precedence grammars. *Scripta Fac. Sci. Natur. UJEP Brunensis Math.* 8 (1978), 1-11.

135. Y. Krevner and A. Yehudai. An iteration theorem for simple precedence languages. Technical Report 81-21, Tel-Aviv University, July 1981.

136. Y. Krevner and A. Yehudai. An iteration theorem for simple precedence languages. In: *Automata, Languages and Programming,* Lect. Notes in Comp. Sci. 140, Springer-Verlag, Berlin, 1982.

137. M.S. Krishamurty and H.R. Rameshehandra. A note on precedence functions. *Information Processing Letters* 4 (1976), 99-100.

138. J. Krol and S. Rokita. Some compiler writing systems. *Podstawy Sterowania* 9 (1979), 381-398.

139. J. Krol, J. Lembas and J. Rosek. Syntactical analysis based on simple precedence grammar (in Polish). *Podstawy Sterowania* 7 (1977), 149-164.

140. J. Krol and P. Wyrostek. Syntax error recovery by means of synchronizing pairs (in Polish). *Podstawy Sterowania* 10 (1980), 109-124.

141. J. Krol. Some error recovery method for precedence parsers (in Polish). *Podstawy Sterowania* 10 (1980), 93-107.

142. W.R. LaLonde and J. des Rivieres. Handling operator precedence in arithmetic expressions with tree transformations. *ACM Trans. Progr. Lang. Syst.* 3 (1981), 83-103.

143. A. Learner and A.L. Lim. A note on transforming context-free grammars to Wirth-Weber precedence form. *Computer Journal* 13 (1970), 142-144.

144. O. LeCarme and G.V. Bochmann. A (truly) usable and portable compiler writing system. In: *Information Processing 1974*. J.L. Rosenfeld (ed.), North-Holland, Amsterdam, 1974, 218-221.

145. H.C. Lee and K.-S. Fu. A stochastic syntax analysis procedure and its application to pattern classification. *IEEE Trans. Computers* C-21 (1972), No.7, July, 660-666.

146. R.P. Leinius. Error detection and recovery for syntax-directed compiler systems. Ph. D. Thesis, Dept. of Computer Science, University of Wisconsin, 1970.

147. B.L. Leong and D. Wotschke. The influence of productions on derivations and parsing. In: 3rd ACM Symposium on *Principles of Programming Languages,* 1976, 1-11.

148. M.R. Levy. Complete operator precedence. *Information Processing Letters* 4 (1975), 38-40.

149. A.L. Lim. Useful algorithms for generating Wirth-Weber grammars for context-free languages. CCD (Imperial College), Research Rep. 72/15, 1972.

150. C.H. Lindsey and S.J. Turner. Precedence grammars for extensible syntax. In: *New Directions in Algorithmic Languages*. S.A. Schuman (ed.), IRIA, France, 1975, 71-88.

151. C.H. Lindsey and S.J. Turner. Two-level grammars for extensible languages. In: *New Directions in Algorithmic Languages*. S.A. Schuman (ed.), IRIA, France, 1976, 9-25.

152. D.B. Lomet. Automatic generation of multiple exit parsing subroutines. In: *Automata, Languages and Programming,* J. Loeckx (ed.), Lect. Notes in Comp. Sci. 14, Springer-Verlag, Berlin, 1974, 214-231.

153. Lu Ru-Qian. The generalized precedence grammar (in Chinese). *Chin. J. Comput.* 4 (1981), 11-20.

154. W.C. Lynch. Ambiguities in Backus Normal Form languages. Ph.D. Thesis, University of Wisconsin, Madison, 1963.

155. W.C. Lynch. A high speed parsing algorithm for ICOR grammars. Andrew Jennings Computer Center, Report Nr.1097, Case Western Reserve University, Cleveland, 1968.

156. D.F. Martin. Boolean matrix method for the detection of simple precedence matrices. *Comm. ACM* 11 (1968), 685-687.

157. D.F. Martin. A Boolean matrix method for the computation of linear precedence functions. *Comm. ACM* 15 (1972), 448-454.

158. G. Mathy. Automatische Fehlerkorrektur von syntaktischen Fehlern in Operatorgrammatiken. Mathematisches Institut, Technische Universitaet Muenchen, Diplomarbeit, 1972.

159. O. Mayer. A framework for producing deterministic canonical bottom up parsers. In: *Mathematical Foundations of Computer Science,* J. Winkowski (ed.), Lect. Notes in Comp. Sci. 64, Springer-Verlag, Berlin, 1978, 355-368.

160. O. Mayer. On deterministic canonical bottom-up parsing. *Information and Control* 43 (1979), 280-303.

161. J. McAfee and L. Presser. An algorithm for the design of simple precedence grammars. *J. Assoc. Comput. Mach.* 19 (1972), 675-698.

162. R.M. McClure. An appraisal of compiler technology. Proc. *AFIPS Spring Joint Computer Conf.,* AFIPS Press, Montvale, N.J., 1972, 1-9.

163. W.M. McKeeman. An approach to computer language design. Tech. Rpt. CS 48, Computer Science Dept., Stanford, Calif., August 1966.

164. W.M. McKeeman, J.J. Horning, E.C. Nelson and D.B. Wortman. The XPL compiler generator system. Proc. *AFIPS Spring Joint Computer Conf.,* 1968.

165. W.M. McKeeman, J.J. Horning and D.B. Wortman. *A Compiler Generator.* Prentice Hall, Englewood Cliffs, N.J., 1970.

166. R. McNaughton. Parenthesis grammars. *J. Assoc. Comput. Mach.* 14 (1967), 490-500.

167. L. Meertens and H. van Vliet. Parsing ALGOL68 with syntax-directed error recovery. In: *ALGOL 68.* Proc. of the 1975 Int. Conf. on ALGOL68. G.E. Hedrick (ed.), Oklahoma State University, Stillwater, June 1975, 118-155.

168. H. Meijer and A. Nijholt. Translator writing tools since 1970: A selective bibliography (June 1982), *SIGPLAN Notices,* to appear.

169. M.D. Mickunas and V.B. Schneider. A comparison of weak precedence, LALR, and bounded context parsing techniques. Manuscript, Purdue University, West Lafayette, Ind., 1973.

170. K.R. Moll. New methods for the treatment of syntax errors in simple precedence languages (in German). Ph.D. Thesis, University of Munich, 1978.

171. K.R. Moll. Left context precedence grammars. *Acta Informatica* 14 (1980), 317-336.

172. J.B. Morris. A result on the relationship between simple precedence languages and reducing transition languages. Proc. Symposium on *Theory of Computing,* ACM, May 1970, 73-80.

173. M. Nagl. *Graph-Grammatiken. Theorie, Anwendungen, Implementierung.* Verlag Friedr. Vieweg & Sohn, Braunschweig-Wiesbaden, 1979.

174. K. Natt and C. Simon. Der EULER-compiler fuer die CD3300. Universitaet des Saarlandes, Saarbruecken, W. Germany, 1972.

175. A. Nijholt. Parsing strategies: A concise survey. In: *Mathematical Foundations of Computer Science,* Lect. Notes in Comput. Sci. 118, M. Chytil and J. Gruska (eds.), Springer-Verlag, Berlin, 1981, 103-120.

176. A. Nijholt. Precedence relations: A bibliography. *SIGACT News,* Vol.14, Nr.2, Spring 1982, 9-19.

177. A.A. Ordjan. GP- and ELR(1)-languages (in Russian). *Z. Vycisl. Mat. Fiz.* 15 (1975), 1289-1297, 1362. [MR 53#12108, 1977]. English translation in: *USSR Comput. Math. and Math. Phys.* (GB) (The total precedence languages and the ELR(1) languages).

178. A.A. Ordjan and G.V. Dzulakjan. Parsing algorithm for indexed languages (in Russian). *Akad. Nauk. Armjan.* SSR Dokl. 69 (1979), Nr.1, 24-29.

179. C. Pair. Arbres, piles et compilation. *Revue Francaise de Traitement de l'Information* 7 (1964), 199-216.

180. M. Paul. Zur Struktur formaler Sprachen. Dissertation, Universitaet Mainz, 1962.

181. A.J. Perlis et al. Internal translator (IT), a compiler for the 650. Carnegie Institute of Technology, Computation Center, Pittsburgh 1956. Reproduced by Lincoln Lab. Div. 6, Document 6D-327.

182. J. Pittl. On LLP(k) grammars and languages. *Theoret. Comput. Sci.* 16 (1981), 149-176.

183. B.W. Pollack (ed.). *Compiler Techniques.* Auerbach Publishers, Philadelphia, 1972.

184. V.R. Pratt. Top-down operator precedence. ACM Symposium on *Principles of Programming Languages,* Boston, Denver, 1973, 41-51.

185. L. Presser. The structure, specifications and evaluation of translators and translator writing systems. Report No.68-51, University of California, Los Angeles, Dept. of Engineering, 1968.

186. L. Presser and M.A. Melkanoff. Transformations to simple precedence. In: Proc. of the Second *Hawaii Int. Conf. on System Science,* Honolulu, 1969.

187. L. Presser. The translation of programming languages. In: *Computer Science,* Cardenas, Presser and Marin (eds.), John Wiley and Sons, New York, 1972.

188. V.A. Pronina. Transformation of grammars to conflictless form. *Avtomat. i Telemekh.* 1974, No.10, 160-165 (Russian); translated as *Automat. Remote Control* 35 (1974), No.10, part 2, 1683-1687 (1975). [MR 56#7352, 1978].

189. V.A. Pronina. Existence of precedence functions for generative grammars. *Automat. Remote Control* 36 (1975), No.7, pt.2, 1165-1168. Translation of: *Avtomat. i Telemekh* (USSR) 36 (1975), No.7, 127-131.

190. V.A. Pronina and A.A. Chudin. Syntax-analysis implementation in an associative parallel processor (Russian). *Avtomat. i Telemekh* 1975, No.8, 106-112; translated as *Automat. Remote Control* 36 (1975), No.8, part 2, 1303-1308 (1976).

191. V.A. Pronina. Parallel syntax analysis. *Automat. Remote Control* 35 (1974), No.7, Pt.1, 1118-1122.

192. J. Reichardt. Analysierbarkeit und Normalformen-Transformation kontext-freier Grammatiken. TI 179, 1979, Technische Hochschule Darmstadt.

193. S.P. Rhodes. Practical syntactic error recovery for programming languages. Ph.D. Thesis, Technical Report 15, Dept. of Computer Science, University of California, Berkeley, Ca., 1973.

194. H. Richter. Syntaxfehlerbehandlung ohne Korrekturversuche (Syntax error recovery without correction attempts). Ph. D. Thesis, University of Munich, LRZ-Bericht Nr. 8204/1, April 1982.

195. B. Rid. Effiziente Implementierung der Suffixanalyse fuer einfache Praeze-denzsprachen. Diplomarbeit, Inst. fuer Informatik, Universitaet Muenchen, 1980.

196. G.D. Ripley. A simple error recovery only procedure for simple precedence parsers. University of Arizona, Tucson Arizone, Dept. of Computer Science, April 1978. Also: *Comm. ACM* 21 (1978), 928-930.

197. S. Rosen (ed.). *Programming Systems and Languages.* McGraw-Hill, New York, 1967.

198. D.J. Rosenkrantz, P.M. Lewis III and R.E. Stearns. A simple language which is not a precedence language. Internal Report, General Electric R&D Center, Schenectady, April 1968.

199. P. Ruzicka. Validity test for Floyd's operator precedence parsing algorithms. In: *Mathematical Foundations of Computer Science,* J. Becvar (ed.), Lect. Notes in Comp. Sci. 74, Springer-Verlag, Berlin, 1979, 415-424.

200. P. Ruzicka. Validity test for Floyd's operator precedence parsing algorithms is polynomial in time. *Kybernetika* 5 (1981), 368-379.

201. M. Schkolnick. Labelled precedence parsing. Conf. Record of ACM Symp. on *Principles of Programming Languages,* Boston, Denver, 1973, 33-40.

202. M.Schkolnick. The equivalence of reducing transition grammars and determi-nistic languages. *Comm. ACM* 17 (1974), 517-519.

203. F. Schwenkel. Partitioned grammars and syntax-analysers. In: *GI-1.Fachta-gung ueber Programmiersprachen.* M. Beckmann, G. Goos and H.P. Kuenzi (eds.), Lect. Notes in Economics and Mathematical Systems 75, Springer-Verlag, Berlin, 1971, 114-139.

204. F. Schwenkel. Precedence syntax directed processor system. User's Manual, University of Notre Dame, Computer Science Department, 1969.

205. S. Sekimoto. Extended right precedence grammars and analyzing techniques for them. *Information Processing in Japan* 12 (1972), 21-25.

206. A.S. Shumei. Syntactical analysis of input text by defining symbols. *Avtomat. i Telemekh* 1971, No. 1, 114-122 (Russian); translated as *Automat. Remote Control* 1971, No.12, Part 2, 1959-1966 (1972).

207. A.S. Shumei. Algorithm for syntactic analysis in a grammar with degenerate precedence matrix. *Avtomat. i Telemekh.* 1973, No.9, 85-90 (Russian); translated as *Automat. Remote Control* 1973, No.9, Part 1, 1440-1444 (1974).

208. A.S. Shumei. Use of weak precedence relationships among defining symbols in a syntactic analyzer. *Cybernetics* (USA) 11 (1975), No.5, 742-750; translation of *Kibernetika* (USSR) 11 (1975), No.5, 77-80.

209. R.K. Shyamasundar. Studies on parsing, syntax-directed translation and conditional grammars. Ph. D. Thesis, School of Automation, Indian Institute of Science, Bargalore, India, 1975.

210. R.K. Shyamasundar. A note on linear precedence functions. *Information Processing Letters* 5 (1976), 81-81.

211. R.K. Shyamasundar. Precedence parsing using Domolki's algorithm. *Int. J. Computer Math.* 6 (1977), 105-114.

212. R.K. Shyamasundar. Precedence-regular grammars. *Int. J. Computer Math.* 7 (1979), 173-186.

213. Softech, Inc. Programmer's guide for building language processors with the AEDJR system. Softech-R-1, March 1970.

214. J. Spielman. Operator and precedence grammars. Unpublished paper, 1964.

215. P. Springer. Automatische Fehlerbehandlung in Sprachuebersetzern mit Hilfe einer Nachsilbengrammatik. Diplomarbeit, Institut fuer Informatik, Technische Universitaet Muenchen, 1976.

216. B.E. Squires. Lexical analysis by a precedence grammar. Univ. of Illinois, Department of Computer Science Report, 1966.

217. M.W. Storm and J.A. Polk. Usage of an XPL based compiler generator system. Proc. 14th Annual *Southeast Regional ACM Conf.*, 1976, 19-26.

218. I.H. Sudborough. A note on weak operator precedence grammars. *Information Processing Letters* 7 (1978), 213-218.

219. G. Terrine. Coordinate grammars and parsers. *Computer Journal* 16 (1973), 232-244.

220. M. Tombah. The elimination of precedence conflicts (Russian). *Trudy Vycisl. Centra Tartu Gos.* Univ. Vyp. 37 (1976), 60-91. [MR 55#9616, 1978].

221. E.A. Trahtengerc and A.S. Shumei. The equivalent transformation of generating grammars to precedence grammars. *Z. Vycisl. Mat. i Mat. Fiz.* 13 (1973), 446-455.

222. E.A. Trahtengerc and A.S. Shumei. The existence of precedence functions for phrase structure grammars (Russian). *Z.Vycisl. Mat. i Mat. Fiz.* 14 (1974), 520-522, 536.

223. G.G. Trubchaninov. Precedence grammars and p-grammars without deadlocks (open-ended) (Russian). *Programmirovanie* 1976, No.1, 27-30, 94. [MR 57#1985, 1979].

224. G.G. Trubchaninov. Classes of grammars oriented on syntactical analysis by the precedence method. *Programmirovanie* 1976, No. 2, March-April, 13-18.

225. E. Ukkonen. A modification of the LR(k) method for constructing compact bottom-up parsers. In: *Automata, Languages and Programming,* H.A. Maurer (ed.), Lect. Notes in Comp. Sci. 71, Springer-Verlag, Berlin, 1979, 646-658.

226. J.D. Ullman. Applications of language theory to compiler design. In: *Currents in the Theory of Computing,* A.V. Aho (ed.), Prentice Hall, Englewood Cliffs, N.J., 1973, 173-218.

227. A. Vooglajd and D. Lijb. Total optimization of the memory of precedence analyzers (in Russian). *Tr. Tallin. Politekh. Inst.* 482, 1980, 3-14.

228. S. Warshall. A theorem on Boolean matrices. *J. Assoc. Comput. Mach.* 9 (1962), 11-12.

229. P. Wegner. The Domolki algorithm. TR 68-18, Dept. of Computer Science, Cornell University, May 1968.

230. F.M. Weingarten. *Translation of Computer Languages.* Holden-Way, Inc., San Francisco, 1973.

231. J.R. White and L. Presser. A structured language for translator construction. *Computer Journal* 18 (1975), 34-42.

232. M.H. Williams. Complete operator precedence conditions. *Information Processing Letters* 6 (1977), 60-62.

233. M.H. Williams. Conditions for extended operator precedence parsing. *Computer Journal* 22 (1979), 164-168.

234. M.H. Williams. A systematic test of extended operator precedence. *Information Processing Letters* 13 (1981), 187-190.

235. N. Wirth. A programming language for the 360 computers. Techn. Report CS-53, Computer Sci. Dept., Stanford University, Stanford, Calif., December 1966.

236. N. Wirth. PL-360: A programming language for the IBM 360 computers. *J. Assoc. Comput. Mach.* 15 (1968), 37-54.

237. N. Wirth and C.A.R. Hoare. A contribution to the development of ALGOL. *Comm. ACM* 9 (1966), 413-432.

238. N. Wirth and H. Weber. Euler- a generalization of ALGOL and its formal definition. Parts 1 and 2. *Comm. ACM* 9 (1966), 13-23 and 89-99.

239. N. Wirth. Algorithm 265: Find precedence functions. *Comm. ACM* 8 (1965), 604-605.

240. N. Wirth. A basic course on compiler principles. *BIT (Nordisk Tidskrift for Informationsbehandling)* 9 (1969), 362-380.

241. D.S. Wise. Generalized overlap resolvable grammars, languages, and parsers. Report #1174, Mathematics Research Center, University of Wisconsin, January 1972.

242. D.S. Wise. Domolki's algorithm applied to a generalized overlap resolvable grammar. Proc. Third Annual Symp. on *Theory of Computing*, 1971, 171-184.

243. D.S. Wise. Generalized overlap resolvable grammars and parsers. *J. Comp. System Sci.* 6 (1972), 538-572.

244. D. Wood. A bibliography of top-down parsing. *SIGPLAN Notices* 13, Nr.2, February 1978, 71-76.

245. D. Wood. *Grammar and L Forms: An Introduction*. Lect. Notes in Comp. Sci. 91, Springer-Verlag, Berlin, 1980.

246. A. Yehudai. A new definition for simple precedence grammars. *BIT (Nordisk Tidskrift for Informationsbehandling)* 19 (1979), 282-284.

247. F.J. Zamecnik. Context resolvable grammars. Ph.D. Thesis, Iowa State University, 1971.

248. R. Zimmer. Weak precedence. Proc. of the *Int. Computing Symposium* 1970, May, Bonn, German Chapter of the ACM, W.D. Itzfeldt (ed.), 1973, 483-491.

249. R. Zimmer. Soft precedence. T.R. Siemens AG, Muenchen, 1970.

250. R. Zimmer. Design of a versatile precedence parsing system. In: *GI-1.Fachtagung ueber Programmiersprachen*. M. Beckmann, G. Goos and H.P. Kuenzi (eds.), Lect. Notes in Economics and Mathematical Systems 75, Springer-Verlag, Berlin, 1971, 79-96.

251. R. Zimmer. Soft precedence. *Information Processing Letters* 1 (1972), 108-110.

TITLES IN THIS SERIES